PRACTICAL
AYURVEDA

PRACTICAL AYURVEDA

SECRETS FOR PHYSICAL, SEXUAL & SPIRITUAL HEALTH

ATREYA

JAICO PUBLISHING HOUSE

Ahmedabad Bangalore Bhopal Bhubaneswar Chennai
Delhi Hyderabad Kolkata Lucknow Mumbai

Published by Jaico Publishing House
A-2 Jash Chambers, 7-A Sir Phirozshah Mehta Road
Fort, Mumbai - 400 001
jaicopub@jaicobooks.com
www.jaicobooks.com

Published in arrangement with
Samuel Weiser, Inc.
P.O. Box 612, York Beach, ME 03910-0612

This edition is for sale in India only.

PRACTICAL AYURVEDA
ISBN 81-7224-811-3

First Jaico Impression: 1999
Seventh Jaico Impression: 2008

Printed by
Repro India Limited
Plot No. 50/2, T.T.C. MIDC Industrial Area
Mahape, Navi Mumbai - 400 710

*In Honor of H. W. L. Poonjaji,
who went into Mahasamadhi on September 6, 1997
so that he could remain forever
in the hearts of those who loved him.
The Satguru is none other than
the heart of all beings.*

*And for my beloved
Girija,
ever pure, daughter of the Himalayas—
without you this book never could have happened.*

Contents

Foreword

Ayurveda, the traditional natural healing system of India, is quickly gaining popularity in the Western world. Interest in the subject has spread rapidly throughout North and South America, Europe, and Australia in recent years. There is a new proliferation of Ayurvedic classes, schools, and treatment centers in most major metropolitan areas. The number of people who are using this ancient health system in their daily lives is becoming considerable. Many people of all walks of life are gaining great personal and spiritual benefit from Ayurveda's wisdom of healing.

The number of books on Ayurveda has also increased, with a steady stream of interesting titles expanding our awareness of this new and profound field of medicine. The Ayurvedic system, like Traditional Chinese Medicine before it, is gradually entering into mainstream health care, being adopted by medical doctors, naturopaths, chiropractors, herbalists and nutritionists. This movement must continue to develop extensively in the coming decades, and can help us deal with the new pressures on our health caused by our modern industrial and high tech life-styles. Ayurveda is not going to be merely a passing health fad, but is an enduring part of the new global paradigm of healing emerging today. We can say that Ayurveda has arrived and is now making its home in the West.

There are many reasons for this new interest in Ayurveda. First, all over the world today we are looking for a natural system of healing that is comprehensive and complete, that is not merely some curious form of folk healing but a real and rational system of medicine that is sensitive to both nature and the Earth. This is exactly what Ayurveda has to offer, for it has a many thousand-year-old clinical tradition and a comprehensive natural method of treatment ranging from diet, herbs, and massage, to life-style counseling and meditation. Ayurveda is not merely East Indian folk medicine but a perennial naturopathic system of health care that has survived through the onslaught of modern medicine and preserved the wisdom of the ages and the wisdom of the Earth.

Second, there is a new search for a mind-body medicine today that is spiritual in nature and addresses the role of consciousness in healing. Meditation and prayer are now recognized for their ability to heal not only the mind but the body. Such a spiritual orientation is everywhere in Ayurveda with its connection to Yogic practices and meditation disciplines and its understanding of the karmic roots of our human problems. Ayurveda always encourages us to a more spiritual life-style and the pursuit of Self-realization, and says that this is essential to our real health and well-being, whatever may be our main pursuit in life.

Third, there are now many people who have studied Yoga and allied spiritual traditions from India and would like to know more about the medical side of that tradition, which is Ayurveda. For this reason most of the Yoga centers and ashrams in the West are now introducing Ayurvedic classes and programs into their activities. Hatha Yoga, the asana side of the Yogic system, has also become very popular worldwide, with Yoga classes offered in nearly every significant community in the United States. Whoever finds this system of exercise helpful will similarly gravitate toward its sister system of Ayurveda. Ayurveda shows how Yogic practices can be used on a therapeutic level for treatment of disease and for health maintenance.

Atreya is well aware of all these trends in his new book on Ayurveda, *Practical Ayurveda: Secrets for Physical, Sexual, and Spiritual Health*, which expands the field of Ayurveda yet further. His writing takes Ayurveda to a deeper level as well as develops it for a larger audience. Atreya is a notable Western student of Ayurveda, who has researched the science in depth in India and has developed much intuitive insight into this ancient system of right living. He has taken a profound interest not only in the healing side of the Vedic tradition but in its spiritual side as well. Most notably, he has deeply examined the non-dual tradition of Self-realization at the summit of the Indic meditational traditions, the system of Advaita Vedanta, and brings this transcendental view into his work.

Atreya approaches Ayurveda not merely looking at its physical aspects, but unfolds, with clarity and precision, its energetic formulations and spiritual principles. This provides a much broader and more flexible perspective on this ancient healing system than usually given, and one that cannot be gained merely by studying the system outwardly. The book has a special emphasis on *prana* or the "Vital force" and is not simply an ordinary presentation of Ayurveda emphasizing physical factors. His approach to Ayurveda is not mechanical or academic but living and experiential, going back to the life-force that is the basis of the Ayurvedic view of life. He examines the entire science of prana, how our life-energy works on all levels of mind and body, a subject he dealt with more specifically in his previous book *Prana: The Secret of Yogic Healing*.

The gross physical body is a manifestation of the subtle energy field of prana, without which we could not even move. Physical imbalances are merely the reflection of earlier imbalances in the pranic field. If we can correct these pranic problems before they manifest in the physical body, we can prevent disease and guard our health. Atreya shows how special pranic methods and ways of using the breath can balance the doshas or biological humors of Ayurveda and reduce the necessity for more complicated or more physical therapies.

Practical Ayurveda is an excellent introduction to the system of Ayurveda and one that is concise, direct, and easy to understand. It covers all the main concepts, practices, and treatments of Ayurveda in a way that is both interesting and informative, both in harmony with the tradition and modern in its understanding. From diet and herbs to daily life-style practices, the book provides Ayurvedic secrets of health and well-being for every major type of person.

Atreya's presentation of Ayurveda is remarkably fresh and filled with his own personal insights, so that other Westerners can follow his lead and way of entry into his often arcane system. Being a Westerner Atreya is able to translate unfamiliar concepts of Ayurveda to the Western mind with lucidity and simplicity. He relates how he uses Ayurveda in his own life and how it has transformed how he lives on all levels. Atreya is an original thinker and adds his own insights about Ayurveda to his book. These can add much in making Ayurveda more practical or accessible to people today for dealing with the changing conditions of our complex modern life.

Without such natural wisdom as Ayurveda, we may find ourselves not only unhealthy, but unhappy and spiritually confused. With Ayurveda we can learn the right diet for our individual type, how to improve our immune system, the keys to right use of sexual energy and rejuvenation, and a conscious way of life that can lift us to a new level of awareness in all our endeavors. May the reader embrace this book as a tool of reintegration with the great healing and transformational energy of prana.

David Frawley
author, *Ayurveda and the Mind,*
Ayurvedic Healing, and *The Yoga of Herbs*
Santa Fe, NM

Introduction

❖ *God requites our actions according as they are good or bad,*
weighing them in the scale of his judgment; the doer reaps
the fruit of his own doings: such is the Vedic principal
and the verdict of mankind. ❖

There is nothing good or bad in Ayurveda. Ayurveda is not
an endless repetition of curries and rigid yogic practices. It
is simply a very ancient, practical method used to understand life. Ayurveda begins by helping people understand
themselves, their unique individual nature. Then it helps
teach people how different natures affect their nature.
This can take the form of food, climate, people, or career.
Ayurveda can be seen as an uncomplicated formula: A +
B = C. In other words, it shows the result of combining
our nature with other objects and places. My personal experience demonstrates this fact for me.

Some years ago I returned to the West to live and
work after living in India for many years. On my return I
found out what stress, anxiety, aspirin and frustration
equals—a duodenal ulcer and a trip to the hospital. I
asked myself, "How could someone who had been meditating for twenty years, who had done years of Western therapy, who worked as a therapist and healer, give himself an
ulcer"? Easy. I hadn't learned to fully accept the reality of
my body and the emotional relationship of mind to the
body. Most importantly, I did not understand my particular constitution—my nature. I also failed to change what I
could in my external affairs to reduce stress. The
Ayurvedic system has taught me these essential lessons
and how to understand my individuality—its strengths
and weaknesses.

By continuing to do activities that over-stressed my
back (I have idiopathic kyphoscoliosis and osteoarthrosis
of the spine) I put myself in tremendous pain and started
a degenerating disease cycle. Wrong action and ignorance
were the root causes. Instead of stopping the aggravating
activity I took aspirin to stop the pain—sound familiar? I
did this because I needed the money that the activity provided. Combined with mental worries about living in
Western society, in addition to other personal frustrations,
the aspirin burned a hole through the wall of the duodenum (small intestine). Although it may seem extremely
stupid to inflict this on myself—it certainly feels stupid to
write it—economic scarcity, emotional unfulfillment, and
mental stress are not uncommon today, nor are they stupid feelings.

Unfortunately, stress caused by something or other is
the reality of many people. My failure was that I didn't
change my situation, nor did I change how I dealt with it
mentally and emotionally. Because I managed to do nothing effective about my condition, everything went wrong at
once, and I finally collapsed on the kitchen floor after
bleeding internally for almost two months. Tests revealed
a red blood cell count of six—normal should be thirteen to
fifteen for a man my age. I was white as a ghost!

All the time I kept thinking that I must have a low
threshold for pain. The direct refusal to acknowledge the
pain in my body—not accepting the reality of my body—
led to a stay in the hospital and several months of conva-
lescing. This is the other side of will power, and we can use
it to kill ourselves, as I almost did by ignoring my body.
This experience forced me to apply Ayurvedic methods
to recover. And now I use Ayurvedic methods to prevent
any future reoccurrence, and to also prevent disease in
general.

Should you be interested in a medical system that
dates back at least 5000 years? Is there really any practical use in using ancient methods of health care? Can the
Ayurvedic system help you in your busy everyday life?

The answer is definitely, yes, to all the above questions. I found out through personal experience that the

Ayurvedic medical system is very applicable today. Had I understood my Ayurvedic constitution I could have avoided all the problems I mentioned. I have now been able to cure myself of a duodenal ulcer, reverse deterioration of the kidneys, correct chronic intestinal problems, and alleviate continuous back pain through Ayurvedic methods. The natural therapies I use have left me healthier, happier, and with a greater knowledge of myself and the universe; and most importantly, of my relationship to that universe. Over the last several years I have been able to share the system with others.

A woman came to me in Paris, where I live, with a combination of several physical problems. She was primarily concerned with her menstruation. After using Ayurvedic diagnostic methods I explained to her the Ayurvedic view of disease and imbalance relating specifically to her constitution. I then suggested that she take a formula of several herbs and avoid eating certain foods. We talked about the psychological implications relating to the present imbalance, and, with these guidelines, I sent her to the pharmacy to buy the correct herbs. I didn't hear anything from her for several months. When I did finally hear about her, it was through another friend whom she sent to me for consultation. All her problems had cleared up within a month, and she had changed certain aspects of her life that were the underlying cause of her physical problems. She was now healthy and happy.

She has taken positive steps to recover her personal power, and has taken responsibility for her health. Her physical disturbances were painlessly and easily alleviated with a formula of eight herbs and KNOWLEDGE— the knowledge of how nature functions and how her body functions in relation to nature. Her problems were easily corrected because she applied that knowledge. What is that knowledge? It has been called Ayurveda, the knowledge of life, for thousands of years. This book is about that knowledge, its origins and the most fundamental component of all life—prana.

Another woman came to me recently because she had been constipated for three days. She had tried everything available—and in France that is a lot of products!—and nothing worked. This had been an ongoing problem for several years and had become quite disabling for this woman of about sixty. Her pulse showed a debilitated liver and an imbalance in the humor that controls movement in the body. She also had a large quantity of toxic accumulation in the body. I recommended two well known Ayurvedic formulas and she received instant relief that same evening. She called me the next day. She was very happy, and now is back on the road to good health. Several weeks of treatment has given her more energy and she is enjoying life again.

Traditional forms of medicine, like Ayurveda and Chinese medicine, were developed by ancient sages. Their astute observations of the universe resulted in the development of "constitutional medicine." The ancients perceived the universe as a constant play of energies, which when imbalanced in the body, lead to discomfort or disease. The role of the ancient doctor was to restore harmony to the body-mind environment. The ancient Vedic culture in India took this concept of constitutional medicine to its highest development in the form of Ayurvedic medicine.

The Chinese and Ayurvedic traditions have developed very sophisticated systems of medicine in the 5000 years of their existence. In fact, Traditional Chinese Medicine, or TCM, still treats one third of the world's population. The United Nations Organization estimates that 70 percent of India's 900 million people are treated by Ayurvedic medicine. Therefore, we can draw the conclusion that constitutional medicine still treats a huge segment of the world's population, even in modern times.

The ancients perceived the universe as different forms of manifested energy; they saw these same fundamental energies in our food and herbs. The unique classification of food and herbs according to their individual actions (or "energies") is how Ayurveda and TCM restore balance to the body. In China a doctor was considered poor or inferior if his patients became sick; for this showed his inability to maintain the harmony of the body with food and herbs. In fact, people only paid the doctor as long as they did not get sick! In Ayurveda, medicine was considered inferior to food and herbs ingested on a daily basis. Actually, medicine was a "last resort" that showed the irresponsibility of the patients' life-styles and habits.

Traditional pharmacology is very highly developed in both the Ayurvedic and TCM systems. They are able to render toxic substances into material safe for human ingestion with relatively simple means. Lacking the technological ability to extract the "active ingredients" of a plant or herb led the ancient doctors to combine several plants that had specific therapeutic effects. Formulas often have fifteen to twenty ingredients in order to achieve the desired therapeutic effect and eliminate any negative side effect. The continuous utilization of these methods of pharmacology attest to their efficiency and safety when administered correctly.

Many ancient cultures traveled to India to learn from India's medical professionals. Traveling Chinese scholars have given us historical records of constitutional medicine in India, although both Ayurvedic and Chinese medical theses still exist from before 1000 B.C. The Four-Humor Theory of the ancient Greeks came from India. We find the Greeks using Ayurvedic theories and herbal formulations after 400 B.C., when they were known to have studied the Ayurvedic system extensively. Hence, it is possible historically to say that constitutional medicine is the foundation of the modern allopathic medicine that evolved from the ancient Greek system. We are actually beginning to come "full circle."

Ayurveda is the mother of all forms of modern medicine, from body work to surgery. Every Occidental and Asian civilization has borrowed Ayurvedic knowledge and applied it to their own cultural context and medical system. Plastic surgery, acupuncture, disease classifications and medical schools all stem from the Ayurvedic tradition. In view of this, Ayurveda, and the information about Ayurveda presented here, should be viewed as complementary to modern allopathic medicine. Ayurvedic therapies can be seen as both physical and psychological preventative measures. In fact, such a view is necessary for the continual growth and harmony of both systems, and for the newly developing concept of global medicine.

This book is based on the oldest surviving medical text of Ayurveda, the Caraka Samhita. *Samhita* means "text" or "thesis" and *Caraka* is the name of the doctor who put the text into its present form. *Caraka* literally means "one who moves around," implying a doctor who moved throughout the country teaching and practicing medicine.[1] The Caraka Samhita primarily covers internal medicine, but it also includes all the basic principles of Ayurvedic medicine.

The Caraka Samhita is a direct transmission of Ayurveda from God or the Creator (Brahma) to a series of enlightened sages ending with the sage Atreya (lit. "son of Atri," who was one of the seven immortal Vedic sages). In the Caraka Samhita, Atreya teaches a group of six disciples, and one of them, Agnivasa, is the actual author of this Samhita. Caraka came a few hundred—or few thousand—years later to actually write down the ancient oral teaching of the sage Atreya. Because of this lineage, historically direct from Brahma, the creator, Ayurveda is considered to be beginningless and endless, therefore an immortal science. Ayurveda's continued relevance today attests to this vision.

It is important to note the modern historical view of Ayurveda versus the far older oral tradition of ancient India. The modern view, according to Christian historians, is that the Caraka Samhita was composed around 1000 B.C. by Agnivasa and then actually written down by Caraka (the person) around 800 B.C. However, ancient oral tradition places the sage Atreya around 5000 B.C., as he is the son of the great immortal seer Atri. Atri is a contemporary of the Vedic seer Vasistha, and of the epic poem, "The Ramayana," in which the avatar Rama destroys Shri Lanka in a war with the evil forces of ignorance. This then places the Caraka Samhita as a 7000-year-old document.

---

[1]Caraka Samhita, vol. 1, R. K. Sharma and Bhagwan Dash, trans. (Varanasi, India: Chowkamba Sanskrit Series Office, 1992), p. xxxvii.

The modern Christian view of history places the first book of Vedic times, the Rig Veda, at about 1500 **B.C.** There are four of these "books" collectively called the Vedas or the "books of knowledge." Ayurveda (*ayur* + *Veda* = the knowledge of life) is considered a sub-Veda, or the branch of knowledge that is concerned with physical health and happiness on Earth, and, therefore, very important for all of us. The Vedas are the basis of the Vedic culture of which Hinduism is a much later manifestation. The oral tradition states that the first of the Vedas was composed about 40,000 years ago.[2] is not the purpose of this book to determine the correct view or the scientifically more accurate view; however, it is necessary to point out that Ayurveda traditionally has very old roots, long before "recorded history."

The oral tradition is still very much alive in India, but unfortunately much of the most valuable information on Ayurveda is passed orally from teacher to student. Due in part to this oral tradition, Ayurveda can appear, at our Western first glance, disjointed, complicated, or simplistic at the same time. However, after deeper study the almost amazing harmony and complete inter-relatedness of the manifested existence become apparent.

The purpose of this book is threefold: to explain Ayurveda to the average person in everyday language; to show the relation of the basic unit of life, prana, to the Ayurvedic system; and to clarify the true spiritual orientation of Ayurvedic healing. It took me some time to grasp the fundamentals of Ayurveda. This was not due to the inherent difficulties of the system, but rather to the language—the presentation and cultural metaphors. Once I was able to surmount these problems it became just a matter of learning any other interesting subject, such as nuclear physics. Hopefully this work will facilitate others

---

[2]This comes from personal dialogs with yogis and teachers in India. For another view on Vedic on Vedic history read Dr. David Frawley, *Gods, Sages and Kings,* or *From the River of Heaven* (Salt Lake City, UT: Passage Press, 1991 and 1990).

in learning Ayurvedic methods, how to apply them in daily life, and how to apply the great spiritual insights of the original founders.

In the United States, several proponents of traditional Eastern medical systems have begun a movement to create a global form of medicine that treats individuals with natural means. This kind of constitutional approach is applicable to everyone throughout the world, and will eventually form the basis of a new global medical system. I wish to thank these persons for helping me learn and assimilate Ayurveda through their writings: Dr. David Frawley, Dr. Vasant Lad, Michael Tierra, Dr. Robert Svobodha, Dr. Frank Ros and Dr. Subhash Ranade, among others.

While this book is another commentary on Ayurveda, the primary focus is to re-examine the role of prana in the healing process. Prana is the most fundamental force in healing, regardless of the tradition. However, Ayurveda fully understands the role of prana. It is the best overall method we can use to promote health and long life. It is with considerable humility that I present this work. I hope that its publication will stimulate the Ayurvedic community in India to release some of the deeper, more profound information on prana that is available there. I hope this information will help to end the commercialization of Ayurveda that turns it into just another form of "symptomatic relief" so prevalent in modern times. If we do not address the total being, and its spiritual source, Ayurveda is not Ayurveda.

I feel that without a deep understanding of our innermost nature, the secrets of Ayurveda are not revealed. What often passes for Ayurveda in India and in the West is nothing like the real Ayurveda that the great seers of ancient times lived and taught. While my teacher is not trained formally in Ayurveda, stories abound of his great healing powers that stem not from intellectual knowledge, but rather from the eternal abidance in his primordial Being or Self. It is he who pointed a finger to the knowledge of Being. It is in this abidance of Being that the true essence of Ayurveda is revealed.

May all beings be at peace.

OM! OM! OM!
MAY THE GRACE OF THE SATGURU
SHINE ON THE FOLLOWING WORDS!
MAY THESE WORDS BE FROM UN-
CHANGING CONSCIOUSNESS AND NOT
LIMITED OR DEFINED BY THE IGNO-
RANCE OF DUAL CONCEPTS!

RAM! RAM! RAM!

SOURCES

All the quotes at the chapter openings in this book are taken from the Motilal Banarsidass version of the Ramayana by Tulsidass, the "Sri Ramacharitamanasa." This version is from the 15th century and is therefore quite recent according to the oral traditions which place the events of the Ramayana at 7000 years ago. Tulsidass rewrote this epic poem to make it more accessible to the ordinary people of India. From the time of writing until today his version is the most popular with the people. Tulsidass was qualified to write or rewrite the story of Rama because he, himself, was a great devotee. I have heard that his own story goes like this:

● ● ●

"Tulsidass was married young, as was the practice of the time; his wife was pretty and younger than he. Tulsidass was obsessed with sex. He was so full of lust that not one day could pass without the desire overwhelming him. For the first several years his young wife did not complain, but soon she became fed up with his endless passion, and asked to cross the river to pay a visit to her family. It was customary for the husband to give permission for his wife to visit her family periodically. Tulsidass refused; he was distressed by the fact that he could not make love for several days while his wife was gone. The young woman, as women will, kept after him until finally he agreed. Tulsidass prolonged as long as possible the inevitable, but, finally one day he had to let her go across the river to visit her family.

The chosen day of departure was in full monsoon and, leaving early in the day, his wife made it across the river. By evening the rains had the river so flooded that the ferry could not cross, nor was there a bridge nearby. Night came and Tulsidass was consumed with lust. He became so mad that he went to the river as one in a dream. Wading out into the raging torrent he began to lose his footing. Flailing his arms he grabbed what, in his delirium, he thought was a tree trunk thrown into the river by the floods. It was, however, the dead body of a villager drowned by the rains. Using the body as a raft, Tulsidass crossed the flooded river and reached the house of his in-laws, who lived not far from the river. Desperately struggling through the rains, mud, and wind, he began to climb the wall to reach his wife's window.

His wife heard someone outside and opened the shutters. There was her mad husband besmeared with mud and wet to the bone! She called out to him to ask how he had managed to cross the river in flood. At that very moment the clouds parted and the moon shown on the river bank, illuminating Tulsidass, the river, and the dead body. The woman cried out in horror, "Tulsidass because of your lust you have used that dead body as your raft! May God have mercy on us! If only you had used one tenth of your lustful desire for God you would now be a saint instead of being cursed!" When Tulsidass heard his wife's words, he awoke from a dream and looked back to see the dead body, as if for the first time.

Struck by his own blind desire, he ran madly into the night. One day, two years later, a saint came to the house of Tulsidass. His wife lived there alone, for Tulsidass had vanished into the storm on that fateful night. She heard a call, and answered it, finding a luminous man patiently standing outside the house. After a moment of silence the saint called her by name and began to bless her. Startled, she realized that it was none other than her husband, Tulsidass, coming back to bless her for turning him toward God.

The chapter quotes given here are from *Tulasidasa's Sri Ramacharitamanasa,* edited and translated by R. C. Prasad (Delhi: Motilal Banarsidass, 1990) as follows: Introduction, p. 248; Chapter 1, p. 645; Chapter 2, p. 189; Chapter 3, p. 290; Chapter 4, p. 210; Chapter 5, p. 656; Chapter 6, p. 100; Chapter 7, p. 622; Chapter 8, p. 657; Chapter 9, p. 657; Chapter 10, p. 301; Chapter 11, p. 625; Chapter 12, p. 272; Chapter 13, p. 649; Chapter 14, p. 662.

1

The Spiritual Aspect of Ayurveda

❖ *The Vedas declare, he said, that you are It, and that*
there is no more difference between It and You than
between water and its ripples. ❖

To understand Ayurveda and its full implications on our
life and health we must look at the spiritual roots from
which it sprang and from which it is inseparable. If a system presents itself as different from these spiritual roots
then it may be a system of medicine, but it certainly is not
Ayurveda as was realized by the creator and the following
tradition of enlightened seers.

> Since consciousness and energy are inseparably one, the
> energy comes into contact with (becomes aware of) the
> Lord and becomes the Lord himself. When the prakriti
> touches the lord she abandons the prakriti-hood (the state
> of being movement). She merges into the Lord even as the
> river merges into the ocean.[1]

Consciousness is the source of all manifestation. As used
in this book, "consciousness" is synonymous with that un-
namable, unknowable source of all experience, or God. The
dual forces of prakriti and purusha arise from and fall
back into consciousness. They arise from consciousness
when consciousness, for no reason, reflects on itself. This
reflection starts a subtle vibration of movement, *shakti.*

---

[1] *Yoga Vasistha: The Supreme Yoga,* vol. II, Swami Venkatesananda, trans.
(Shivanandanagar, India: The Divine Life Society, 1976, 2nd ed., 1991), p.
589.

The immortal sages state: The only reality is the infinite, unchanging consciousness. And the sage Vasistha states:

> Consciousness is never without some movement within itself. Without this movement it might become "unreal" (unknown). . . . Movement is the very nature of consciousness and therefore inseparable from it.[2]

This is Shiva and Shakti—consciousness and energy—but energy is not consciousness as Vasistha now points out.

> However, motion or action cannot be regarded as the quality of consciousness because it has no qualities nor characteristics: consciousness is pure and utterly tranquil, beyond all description. [And yet, he states] Just as motion within space is experienced by us as air, even so the dynamic energy of consciousness is experienced by the action or motion that takes place in that consciousness.[3]

Cosmic prana is often called shakti. Thus the principle of movement, of motion on the most fundamental level—even before creation—is prana. Creation can now begin because of the two fundamental components: consciousness and the dynamic energy of consciousness. This is prakriti and purusha. Prana continues to become more tangible in the form of prakriti. "... it is the dynamic energy of consciousness that is known as prakriti. . . . That which is superior to this energy (prakriti) is consciousness itself which is the very self of consciousness, supreme peace." [4]
    What then is purusha? Well, this is where the sages show how subtle their perception of life—of reality—was (and in some cases still is). Purusha is also consciousness, it is pure consciousness that cannot be grasped in any way but can only be experienced. Vasistha describes it like this: "It is full of non-consciousness and objectless conscious-

---

[2] *Yoga Vasistha: The Supreme Yoga*, vol. II, p. 586.
[3] *Yoga Vasistha: The Supreme Yoga*, vol. II, p. 587.
[4] *Yoga Vasistha: The Supreme Yoga*, vol. II, p. 589

ness, it can only be indicated by negation. . . . That state is the void, Brahman, Consciousness, the Purusha . . ."[5] In other words, these two are again nothing more than God. One is consciousness in a dynamic manifestation, and the other is consciousness in a void, un-manifestation. Both are needed, both are different aspects of the same thing; they are the substratum of everything. They are not two, but one; experienced as neverending peace and joy. This is the underlying nature of everything; this consciousness is our nature, our substratum.

When these two, prakriti and purusha, begin to interact, they create an individualized awareness. When this awareness begins to reflect on itself, the manifestation is created.

On account of a slight movement of thought, the same reality which is consciousness seems to become the fivefold elements and thence the body. In the same way, the same consciousness becomes worms and other creatures, metals and minerals, earth and what is on it, water and other elements. Thus, the whole world is nothing but the movement of energy in consciousness which appears as the fivefold elements.[6]

We see that the five states of matter, or the five elements, which form the basis of Ayurveda are nothing more than movement in consciousness. That movement in its most subtle form is none other than consciousness, but once conscious of itself, it generates cosmic prana or shakti— the inseparable dynamic aspect of consciousness—and the creation starts. Without prana nothing is possible.

What then is responsible for the different manifestations of the five states of matter in relation to worms and humans? How does a person become a person and a worm become a worm? Vasistha relates the cause to the latent

---

[5] *Yoga Vasistha: The Supreme Yoga*, vol. I, p. 324.
[6] .*Yoga Vasistha: The Supreme Yoga*, vol. II, p. 440.

impressions, *vasanas*, that become activated by the conscious-prana as creation occurs.

The chit-shakti (consciousness-energy) lies in immobile creatures, etc., as latent vasana. It is this chit-shakti that determines the nature of each object; it is the fundamental characteristic of the very molecules of each object. [7]

Vasistha then is telling us that these latent impressions, or vasanas, are really a unique combination of consciousness-energy. I have talked about vasanas and their psychological effects on people in my first book, *Prana: The Secret of Yogic Healing*.[8] In Vedic thought—which is the origin of Yogic, Hindu and Ayurvedic philosophies—the vasanas are the cause of unhappiness, rebirth, psychological disorders, and many other problems, including bad health. These vasanas are anything that conditions or imposes a concept on the substratum of consciousness-energy, our true nature. An example is the idea, "I am limited to the physical body."

> If this (chit-shakti, vasana) is not realized as atma-shakti (the energy of infinite consciousness) it creates the delusion of world-appearance; if it is realized as the truth, which is infinite consciousness, that realization destroys all sorrow.[9]

Perhaps I should say that Vasistha is one of the seven immortal sages of the Vedic period. He has the most hymns in the oldest Veda, the Rig Veda, and is the foremost of all the Vedic sages. I strongly suggest reading Dr. David Frawley's book *Gods, Sages, and Kings*,[10] for a very inspir-

---

[7] *Yoga Vasistha: The Supreme Yoga*, vol. I, p. 351.

[8] Atreya, *Prana: The Secret of Yogic Healing* (York Beach, ME: Samuel Weiser, 1996).

[9] *Yoga Vasistha: The Supreme Yoga*, vol. I, p. 351.

[10] David Frawley, *Gods, Sages* and *Kings* (Salt Lake City, UT: Passage Press,1991). See page 59 for comments on Vasistha.

ing understanding of this period of history and a new interpretation of the Rig Veda.

I had the chance to visit a cave in the Himalayas where Vasistha was reputed to have lived and meditated for a long period of time. It is located above Rishikesh very near the banks of the Ganga (Ganges). It was a very small and narrow cave; my six foot frame was only able to enter by stooping. I could see nothing except utter black— blacker than black. I entered and stopped after twenty feet or so and waited for my eyes to adjust to the darkness. After five minutes I went forward with two other companions, feeling the cold damp wall all the way because I still could not see anything. Another twenty to thirty feet in the cave we found an altar with a few ghee (clarified butter) lamps burning, flowers, pictures, and incense. It was not visible before due to a natural curve in the cave. We sat for quite some time; I had no inclination to meditate, to inquire into the nature of reality or myself. There was no movement in my mind. There was a deep profound peace pervading my being, a happiness that spontaneously arose to pervade everything. It was not cosmic, dramatic, or even experiential, I was just incredibly happy sitting there in this dark cave. After some time another person arrived and I left, taking this happiness outside to Ganga where I spent the next few hours swimming. That happiness pervades to this day some two years later.

These teachings are very profound, often quite subtle. The bottom line of Vasistha's teaching is that you are unlimited, unconditioned, pure consciousness now, without doing anything. It is the conditioning of this fundamental truth that gives rise to vasanas. The Laghu Yoga Vasistha is a condensed version of Vasistha's teaching—the complete book is the third longest in the world—compiled by Abhinanda, a Kashmir scholar. In it he gives us a brief (by Indian standards!) explanation about the latent impressions and conditionings called vasanas, and how they cause us problems. Interestingly, all of the dialogs in the Yoga Vasistha are given as a verbal teaching from Vasistha to his disciple, the avatar Rama of the Ramayana.

Here Rama asks what is the basic cause of ignorance and unhappiness (samsara).

> The seed for this samsara or world-appearance is the body, O Rama. . . . The seed for this body is the mind which is dominated by hopes and desires. . . . There are two seeds for the mind: one, the movement of the prana or life-force, and two, mental conditioning which is deep-rooted. When the life-force moves along the subtle channels of the psychic force, then awareness and experience arise and the mental activity commences. Though this awareness exists everywhere, it is activated by the movement of the life-force. Therefore, it is best to restrain this experience. . . . Therefore, if you restrain the movement of prana and prevent the expansion of the field of objective experience which results from the movement of the mental conditioning (vasanas) then you will go beyond samsara (misery).[11]

OK, so we know now that prana and vasanas are the cause of our miseries, unhappiness, and ignorance because they create what we call "mind," and mind gives rise to the idea that we are limited to the physical body. Well, how exactly do these vasanas get formed in our body for the prana to activate them?

Vasistha explains it as follows. A vasana or mental conditioning is developed when we see an object and—without inquiring into its fundamental nature—decide that it is "something." How firmly we hold on to the idea of the object perceived either gives it life or not. For example, if I firmly believe I will get sick from being around someone who has a cold, I will create a mental conditioning (vasana) that correspondingly will weaken my immune system so that I can get sick. Conviction toward any concept gives reality to that concept. We then get overpowered by the concept, perceive it as reality, and are deluded. When we abandon our true unconditioned nature we are deluded, and this is known as mind, or the basic mental/

---

[11] *Yoga Vasistha: The Supreme Yoga,* vol. II, p. 745.

emotional functioning of a person. Mind is not our basic nature. That is intelligence or intellect. When we are "deluded" we lose sight of the substratum of the object and place reality on the object itself. This is just a simple mistake of not perceiving the substratum, consciousness. All things exist due to this consciousness: it is not that things do not exist or that they are unreal. Vasistha, instead, says that everything is the same—God, because "God" is the source of all manifestation as described above. Therefore, the solution to unhappiness, misery, psychological problems, and ultimately physical problems is to look for the substratum in all things—unconditioned consciousness or God.

The basic concepts of body and mind are not perceived correctly due to prana and vasanas. By learning to control prana, or by dissolving vasanas, we can bring the mind to an unconditioned state in which consciousness alone is perceived.

> As long as the mind is not quiet, the conditioning does not cease; unless the conditioning ceases, the mind does not reach the state of quiescence. . . . Study of scriptures dealing with self knowledge, company of holy ones, the abandonment of mental conditioning and also the control of prana—these are the methods for the control of the mind.[12]

This then gives us a practical way in which to overcome daily problems of living on all levels of our life. The physical body will generally be the last to benefit directly. However, Ayurveda says that if the other more subtle aspects of our being are not addressed, true health will not materialize. Understanding the basis of how the universe and humans are created clarifies the relationship of emotional and psychological disturbances in our life and health. The practical method stated above is threefold: knowledge, a quiet mind and elimination of vasanas. All three are

---

[12]*Yoga Vasistha: The Supreme Yoga,* vol. II, p. 748, 749.

inter-related. Prana can be used to quiet the mind and so eliminate the mental conditionings that prevent knowledge.
Just how important is prana to our health? To Ayurveda?

> Life ebbs away on account of the movement of prana or the life force. If the movement of prana can be arrested, longevity is gained. If one is able to banish movement of thought or movement of prana, he is also able to banish decay and death to a great extent.[13]

In Yoga, and ultimately Ayurveda, the pattern of disease is clearly described in relation to the preceding information. Diseases and psychological disorders are considered to be a major cause of sorrow and unhappiness. Sometimes the physical and mental disorders are related, sometimes not, but both are due to ignorance. Ignorance leads to bad mental habits and poor, irregular routines for the body, which in turn causes disease. Ayurveda provides us with both physical and mental routines with which we can balance prana and break destructive mental and physical habits.

As Ayurveda is based on the actions of the five elements, so, too, Vasistha sees the five elements as the root of disease and the way to overcome it. "All these psychic disturbances and physical ailments arise from the five-fold elements."[14]

Physical ailments are divided into two categories—ordinary and serious. The ordinary ones can be corrected by a change in daily routine, including diet and exercise. The serious ailments and mental disorders are not truly corrected until self-knowledge is recognized. "Self-knowledge ends all physical and psychic disturbances. However, physical ailments that are not psychosomatic may be

---

[13]*Yoga Vasistha: The Supreme Yoga,* vol. II, p. 744..
[14]*Yoga Vasistha: The Supreme Yoga,* vol. II, p. 442.

dealt with by medication, prayers, by baths, and by right action."[15]

How do physical ailments occur due to mental disturbances? Mental confusion, or the inability to function without stress, agitates the prana, which then flows unevenly along the channels or *nadis*. This haphazard or uneven flow results in the congestion of some nadis and the depletion of others. This creates a disturbance in the metabolic process. "Then there arises disturbance in the metabolism, indigestion, excessive appetite and improper functioning of the digestive system. Food eaten turns to poison. The natural movement of food in and through the body is arrested. This gives rise to various physical ailments."[16]

This is why Ayurveda places so much stress on the health of the digestive system. When the digestive system is maintained in correct balance, then mental afflictions will not be able to unbalance the pranic flow enough to cause damage. Even if the pranic flow is disturbed, it will only be for a temporary period of time, if one follows correct daily eating and living habits.

There are clearly two levels in which to perceive this information. The first is the Yogic concept that ignorance leads to both physical and mental illness. "Ignorance" translates, in this case, as responsibility on a mundane level. If we follow correct living habits—eating, exercising, and living correctly for our personal constitution—then the possibility for ailments to occur will be greatly diminished or eliminated. We can call it common-sense or responsibility, but it is simply doing the right thing for our body.

The other level in which to perceive the above information is from an "absolute" point of view. This utilizes Vasistha's perspective that everything is Consciousness (God) because everything manifests out of consciousness. This is called Self-Knowledge by the sages because if

---

[15] *Yoga Vasistha: The Supreme Yoga,* vol. II, p. 442...
[16] *Yoga Vasistha: The Supreme Yoga,* vol. II, p. 442..

everything is consciousness, then obviously you are, too. Knowledge of the Self (God) means that everything is God (Self) including you. Your fundamental state of being is, "I exist," and this we call "self." This is the knowledge of unity, the substratum, the common denominator in all existence or the "self" of all. Hence, the term Self-Knowledge or the knowledge of God existing in all things.

The sages who created Ayurveda and Yoga knew that this Self-Knowledge was and is the ultimate cure to all unhappiness and misery. This knowledge is the ultimate medicine. When you have realized the unchanging unity of all creation, there occurs a kind of health that is unsurpassed by any other kind of health. The ancient sages called it *sat-chit-anand* or being-consciousness-bliss. By just being as you are—consciousness—bliss results. These timeless moments of absorption in pure being are truly what gives health in your life. The quality of happiness and joy that are the undercurrent in your life are due to this Self-Knowledge. However, if a perfect body and physical health are desired in addition to this kind of health, then learn to master the prana in the body.

The prana and apana can be balanced and held in perfect equilibrium. If you achieve this, immortality can result; food becomes unnecessary and you live by absorbing the cosmic prana directly from the air. There are many stories substantiating this fact, some recorded by science and unexplainable. For example, in the early 1900s, a yogi was buried underground for fifteen years. This was well-documented and witnessed by the official community. After fifteen years only one of the witnesses was alive to have the yogi dug up. He was alive, looked well and lived for another ten years before leaving his body. Yogis are able to do this because they can absorb the prana directly into their bodies. I have a friend who personally witnessed this in the Himalayas in the early 1970s. He checked to see if there was any kind of tube or hose for the yogi to breathe through; he found none. The yogi was buried for one month and looked more vital after being buried than before! Although, this shows a high state of development in pranic control, it may not show Self-Knowledge. One may lead to the other or not. In the ancient texts Self-Knowledge is regarded as the supreme attainment, while the control of prana results in immortality and psychic powers. Vasistha says, "I shall now describe to you the method of gaining what is attainable (siddhi or psychic powers) towards which the sage of self-knowledge is indifferent, which the deluded person considers desirable and which one who is intent on the cultivation of self-knowledge is keen to avoid."[17] He then spends several pages telling us how to attain immortality, and powers such as levitation, bi-location, the ability to fly, and how to change your size; all through manipulating prana or kundalini. "Kundalini functions in the body composed of the fivefold elements, in the form of the life-force."[18]

I am often asked in workshops why many of the spiritually illuminated persons of modern history die of some serious disease. Many have died of cancer (Ramakrishna, Ramana Maharishi, etc.) or other serious illnesses. There are two explanations for this. The first is that once a person knows the unity of all beings, he or she ceases to be concerned with his or her own body. The prana slowly begins to dissolve and merge back into its origin—consciousness. This can take a lifetime, sixty to seventy years, or a few days. It depends on the *parabdha* of the person. *Parabdha* means "that which is already underway." Or it is described like this: the archer aims the arrow at the deer, his target; he shoots the arrow; a moment after releasing the arrow, he realizes that the target is not a deer, but a person. He cannot now bring back the arrow and so must face the consequence of the action even after realizing the truth of the situation. This is parabdha karma. Yet, the seers say that there is no parabdha for one who knows, because there ceases to be any one individual to identify with that parabdha. Another way to say this is that it is

---

[17]*Yoga Vasistha: The Supreme Yoga,* vol. II, p. 438.
[18]*Yoga Vasistha: The Supreme Yoga,* vol. II, p. 441.

destiny. Destiny accounts for roughly ten to fifteen percent of all of our diseases.

The second explanation is that once students gather around a person who has ceased to identify with himself or herself as an individual, but rather as Consciousness, a secondary effect happens. This effect is that of a magnet. The vasanas of the students begin to leave their bodies (including the subtle bodies) and collect onto the teacher. This all happens without any direct action by either the students or the teacher. Consciousness acting through the teacher (Self-realized being) wishes to help the students by removing their vasanas. It is the vasanas (mental conditioning) which prevent us from perceiving the substratum. Therefore, if they are removed, Self-Knowledge will result.

This secondary effect may be why many illuminated persons live alone or quietly. My teacher lived for fifty years after realization without allowing people to collect around him for long periods of time. This is also why some of these people die of cancer or other diseases. The vasanas can accumulate and slowly the teacher suffers the consequences of those mental impressions and karmas. It is the sum total of the students' mental conditionings, vasanas, that cause major diseases to manifest on realized people. There are undoubtedly other factors that I am not aware of, but these are the two most commonly occurring reasons. It is also reasonable to suggest that some karmic disposition toward the disease must remain in the subtle bodies of the sage for the actual manifestation to occur. However, this last statement is my conjecture and may not be the case.

In conclusion, several factors must be reviewed. First, prana is inseparable from pure consciousness or God. This pure consciousness is the substratum of all existence and therefore the pure nature of every being. The special combination of consciousness-prana determines each individ0-ual manifestation of the substratum. This special combination when viewed as limited (conditioned) results in an impression called a vasana which covers the substratum. This same special combination, when viewed as the substratum, results in Self-Knowledge. The movement of prana activates the vasanas and together the two create the mental process that we call mind. Mind then wrongly identifies the body as the substratum and ignorance is born. With the advent of ignorance we make poor decisions and the pranas are disturbed. This disturbance imbalances the metabolism which causes the digestion to malfunction. Our food turns toxic and sickness results.

Understanding our substratum or fundamental nature is then the most basic form of health care that one can pursue. As the ancient seers of the past have concluded, true health lies in Self-Knowledge, as it is the root of all other occurrences in the manifestation.

2

Prana in Ayurveda

❦ *After taking the first five morsels, with the repetition of*
the five mantras, pranaya svaha, apranaya svaha,
vyanaya svaha, udanaya svaha, samanaya svaha, directed to the
five vital breaths of the body which are prana, apana,
samana, vyana, and udana . . . ❦

The secret of unlocking the practical application of Ayurveda in everyday life is to understand that ever-elusive, ever-present force—prana. Prana is the source of all manifested matter, and it is important to understand its actual role in the manifestation. Ayurveda is primarily a pranic system of medicine. The basis of the constitutional methodology in Ayurveda rests with the five elements, or five states of matter. These five material states (explained in chapter 3) originate from prana. Therefore, by understanding prana one can understand the primary basis for the Ayurvedic perception.

Prana has many names in the Vedic tradition: Vayu, Vata, Varat, Hiranyagarbha, Shakti, Prakruti, and even Purusha. Innumerable systems of philosophy developed out of the Vedic tradition and often use different terms to describe the same concept, or use the same term to mean very different concepts. These differences confuse Westerners who do not understand Sanskrit. However, prana is worshipped as the cause of life and death, as the god of gods, as the force which maintains life, as life itself. Prana is synonymous with life.

Prana is the cosmic principle of movement or energy. It is seen as the underlying cause of all the manifestation. Prana is the most subtle element of existence; yet it is the most apparent in its manifestation around us. Prana empowers all other forces in the universe, everything else is dependent on it, even creation itself. Prana is eternal movement, empowering the ever-changing cosmos.

> The god Vayu is the eternal cause of the universe: He brings existence as well as destruction to all living beings. He causes happiness and misery. He is the god of death, controller, Lord of creatures. . . . He possesses innumerable forms. He can move everywhere, and is responsible for all actions and thoughts. He is subtle and omnipresent. He is the Lord Vishnu. He has permeated the whole universe. The god Vayu alone has the above distinctive features.[1]

Prana has many different manifestations, from the most subtle to the gross manifestation of electricity. It is the power which enables us to think, feel, and hear. It is the first sound—OM. It manifests in the body as the five pranas: prana, udana, samana, apana and vyana. These five pranic forces govern all types of movement in the body; they restrain and impel mental activity, coordinate the senses, help in the enjoyment of their objects; they hold together different parts of the body, promote speech, enable touch and hearing; they are the cause of joy and courage; they stimulate digestion, absorb the three humors, expel waste from the body; they create the gross and subtle channels in the body, mold the shape of the embryo, and determine the length of the life span.[2]

The traditional locations and actions of the five pranas are shown in figure 1 on page 17.

•Prana—Inward moving prana—seated in the head and heart—controls thinking, emotion, sensory functioning, and memory. We receive cosmic prana from the sun; it is called hot or solar prana.

•Apana—Downward moving prana—seated in the colon—controls the process of elimination (urine, sweat,

---

[1]Caraka Samhita, vol. I, R. K. Sharma and Bhagwan Dash (Varanasi, India: Chowkamba Sanskrit Series Office, 1992), p. 239..

[2]Caraka Samhita, vol. 1, p. 237.

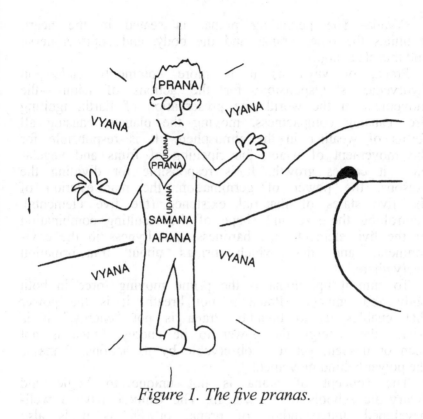

Figure 1. The five pranas.

menstruation, orgasm, and defecation), and receives prana from the Earth and Moon; It is called cool, or lunar, prana.

•Samana—Equalizing prana, seated in the navel, controls the digestion and harmonizes prana and apana. This is also called the upward breath, for together with apana it creates the upward and downward movement of breathing.

•Udana—Upward-moving prana—located in the throat—controls speech, connects us to the solar and lunar forces (sky and Earth), is responsible for spiritual development, controls psychic powers and psychic phenomena, and controls creative expression. The development of kundalini relates directly to udana prana.

•Vyana—The pervading prana, is seated in the heart; it unites the other pranas and the body, and controls nerve and muscle action.

Prana, or vayu as it is more commonly called in Ayurveda, is responsible for the actions of nature—the movement in the world, the preservation of Earth, igniting fire, causing compactness, moving the planets, causing all forms of weather in the atmosphere. It is responsible for the movement of water, the ripening of fruits and vegetables; it causes growth. It is responsible for dividing the seasons, the power of germination, the manifestation of the five states of material existence (the five elements), controlling the size and shape of the resulting combination of the five elements, the hardness and dryness in the environment, and that which brings about transformation everywhere.[3]

To sum it up, prana is the prime moving force in both body and universe. Prana is not breath, it is the power that enables us to breathe. Prana is not "energy," it is what gives energy the power to be energy. Prana is not seen or unseen, yet it is observable by its actions. Prana is the power behind movement.

The concept of prana is not unique to Yogic and Ayurvedic schools of knowledge. The Chinese have a well-developed understanding of prana, or Qi as it is also named. However, the Chinese have a slightly different view of the creation, and their description of Qi is also somewhat different. "Chinese thought does not distinguish between matter and energy, but we can perhaps think of Qi as matter on the verge of becoming energy, or energy at the point of materializing."[4] Yet there are far more similarities than differences. The oldest and primary book of Chinese medicine is the *Nei Ching.* Here is an ancient account of Qi from that book.

[3]Caraka Samhita, vol. 1, p. 238.
[4]Ted J. Kaptchuk, *The Web That Has No Weaver* (Chicago: Congdon & Weed, 1983), p. 35.

The root of the way of life, of birth and change is Qi; the
myriad things of heaven and earth all obey this law. Thus
Qi in the periphery envelops heaven and earth, Qi in the
interior activates them. The source where from the sun,
moon, and stars derive their light, the thunder, rain wind
and cloud their being, the four seasons and the myriad
things their birth, growth, gathering and storing: all this
is brought about by Qi. Man's possession of life is completely dependent upon this Qi.[5]

Therefore, we can see that the two most ancient surviving
cultures have the same basic concepts of prana. They applied these concepts to all aspects of life and did not limit
its usage to medical systems. Understanding prana (or
vayu) helps us understand many of the strange—for the
Western mind—concepts of Ayurveda or Chinese medicine.
Prana is, in fact, one of three cosmic forces that ancient
sages perceived in the universe.

Even Brahma the creator, though he presides over the
universe which is unimaginably vast and which is his
body, exists in an atom; in fact, he does not occupy any
space at all. . . . but in truth, 0 Rama, he is but pure consciousness. Because this consciousness becomes aware of
motion, it experiences such motion or life-force. This is
the prana and the apana whose whirling motion comes to
be known as wind in the universe, which is the very heart
of the universe. The exudations, as it were, of this prana
are known as vata or wind, pitta or heat and slesma
(kapha) or moisture (the three humors of the body) and
their cosmic counterparts—wind, sun and moon.[6]

This clearly shows that prana is the source of the three
Ayurvedic humors—vata, pitta and kapha. "First of all,

[5]Nei Ching, as quoted in Dr. Stephen Chang, The Complete Book of
Acupuncture (Delhi, India: Surjeet Publications, 1982), p. 17.
[6]Yoga Vasistha: The Supreme Yoga, vol. II, Swami Venkatesananda, trans.
(Shivanandanagar, Uttar Pradesh, India: The Divine Life Society, 1991, 2nd
ed.), p. 575.

there is a principle of energy that gives force, velocity, direction, animation, motivation. . . . The second of the triad of forces they perceived as a principle of light, or radiance. . . . The third of these forces was seen as a principle of cohesion. . . . These three are one; life is light, which is love. The energetic principle (life), possesses a radiance (light), which in turn has a bonding power (love)."[7] These three cosmic forces, in essence three different aspects of the same consciousness, can be described as life, light, and love, or as the wind, sun, and moon metaphorically.

This description of energy, transformation, and cohesion really helped me understand the unity of Prana with the other primordial cosmic forces of creation—*Agni* and *Soma*. *Agni* (light) and *Soma* (love) can be related to the Chinese concepts of Yang and Yin respectively. The two polarities are always interacting and interrelating with each other because they are not two, but one. Prana can be related to the concept of Qi or Chi, that which empowers the other two. Agni relates to fire, the sun, transformation and expansion, the humor pitta, and it has masculine properties. Soma relates to liquid, the moon, cooling, unifying, feminine properties, and the humor kapha. Pure Consciousness is the source of these three universal principles or forces, but is not separate from them.

As stated before, the term "consciousness" is synonymous with God, not the God of any religion (Christian, Islam, Hindu or other), but rather the source of all these gods humans have created in their own limited ability to comprehend the unlimited, the uncomrehendable. In its purest sense, each religion defines "God" to be the source of all creation—simple purity of being. It refers to a state that is stateless yet completely aware and conscious.

> One should contemplate the Lord in the following manner: he is the light illuminated by the solar force as well

---

[7]Dr. David Frawley, *Ayurvedic Healing* (Salt Lake City, UT. Passage Press, 1989), pp. 3-4.

as the lunar force, he is the intelligence that eternally lies hidden in all material substances, he is the extrovert awareness that flows through the bodily avenues on to the external world, he is the prana that moves in one's nose, he transforms contacts of the senses into meaningful experiences, he rides the chariot composed of prana and apana, he dwells in secret in the cave of one's heart. He is knower of the knowable and the doer of all actions, the experiencer of all experiences, the thinker of all thoughts.[8]

As the basis for all the manifested creation, prana is worshipped as the "lesser Brahma" or Hiranyagarbha. This is the aspect of cosmic consciousness that—together with transformation and cohesion—actually starts the creation process.

The Lord of all creatures is Prana, whose movement in the womb of creation gives birth to the images of all beings in your likeness, yet remaining ever the one unchanging. It is you, prana, alone who endows the power to the senses, everything is perceived through you, for this all creatures bring you gifts.[9]

Prana and the other two forces are always together and never function alone, although they can be perceived as separate. They are, in fact, one phenomenon that arises simultaneously out of consciousness. In Ayurveda prana is the controlling force in the body.

Ayus ("life") is the combination of body with Prana brought forth by adrsta ("the unseen or unmanifest"). Prana has twelve components—three dosas (humors),

---

[8]*Yoga Vasistha: The Supreme Yoga,* vol. II, p. 392.
[9]Prasna Upanishad, chapter 2, verse 7. My transliteration. Note: Many translations exist in English, each differing somewhat in meaning. Please refer to bibliography for different translations.

three *gunas* (qualities; sattva, rajas and tamas), five
senses, and atman (individualized consciousness).[10]

The biological humors are merely three different statuses
or orientations of the life-force (prana).[11]

Prana is perceived differently on many levels, and the
view changes depending on the stance you take. Therefore, the ancient scriptures provide many diverse names
and actions that are attributed to the principle of energy
or movement. As diverse as these names and actions
may seem, there are several universal themes throughout
all the different scriptures and texts over thousands of
years. They are: prana is life, without prana there is no
life on any level of existence; without prana everything
else is inert; in the physical body, prana is interrelated to
the mental process, or thinking; in the physical body
prana provides the binding power, and at death the prana
ceases to bind the soul to the body; prana controls the
three humors; and prana is the dominant force in the
body.

Vayu or vata is one of the three biological humors of
the body, and as the most direct manifestation of prana, it
is the controlling humor. Vayu provides energy to the other
two humors—pitta and kapha. Without vayu (prana) the
other two humors are dead. Therefore, vayu is often called
the most important humor. In the Caraka Samhita this is
exemplified by the chapters titled "Eighty diseases caused
by Vata," and "Forty diseases caused by Pitta," and
"Twenty diseases caused by Kapha." These do not classify
all the possible diseases, but do provide a listing of the
most prevalent illnesses. As one can see, vata is double the
quantity of pitta, and pitta is double the quantity of
kapha.

---

[10]Priya Vrat Sharma, **Sodasangahrdayam:** *Essentials of Ayurveda* (New
Delhi, India: Motilal Banarsidass Publishers, 1993), p. 3.

[11]Dr. David Frawley, *Ayurvedic Healing,* p. 109.

Because prana is without substance, its manifestation in the body as vayu or vata is also insubstantial. This means it is also the most unstable; like wind it is ever changing. It is usually the first humor to go out of balance due to its special relationship with prana. Having now understood that prana is the source of the five elements and three biological humors, we can proceed to learn more about the specific manifestations of prana as the five states of matter and three humors.

3
Constitution

❖ *Then Vasistha, the sage, narrated various legends befitting the*
occasion, and dispersed the gloom that hung over them all—
by the light of his own spiritual wisdom. ❖

To understand the three humors of Ayurveda we must first understand the fundamental differences between the Ayurvedic system and the modern Western medical system—allopathy. The older system looks at each person as a whole, and treats disorders as a total phenomenon of that whole. Modern medicine has developed from an analytical point of view, and believes that the whole can be understood from its parts. Therein lies the difference: one system says it is impossible to understand the whole from its parts and the other says that it is possible.

CONSTITUTIONAL MEDICINE
Ancient Greeks and Europeans used a constitutional system of medicine. The Greeks traveled to India over a period of several centuries, studying, among other things, Ayurveda. They developed a system based on four constitutional types. In certain parts of the Middle East, this system is still in use.

What is constitutional medicine? It simply means that you are born with a certain combination of principles or forces that determine your individuality. These forces were called humors in ancient Greece and Europe. In Ayurveda they are called the *tridosha*, which means the "three humors." The balance of these forces (or humors) determines your constitution. Your personality is a direct reflection of

your constitution. Your body and mind are also a direct reflection of your constitution. The combination of these
three pranic forces creates you—a unique individual.

The advantage of using a constitutional system of
medicine is that you are diagnosed and treated as an individual. Statistics and averages lose much of their importance in this form of medicine. You are much more likely to
be treated according to your personal needs, rather than
as a percentage.

Another advantage is that constitutional medicine is
not overly concerned with the symptoms of disease, but
with eliminating the imbalance in the humors that is
causing the symptoms. This leads to a real quality of
health. This process of re-balancing the constitution can
take a considerably longer period of time than allopathic
(Western medicine) treatments. The difference is that the
well being achieved through balancing the constitution is
permanent and will often eliminate other seemingly unre-
lated diseases or symptoms.

Constitutional medicine requires your own effort, you
are not dependent on unknown agents. Working with this
form of treatment includes a re-education process, for you
will learn to live in harmony with your nature. You learn
how to eliminate disease and maintain your natural balance, and this is the best insurance against ill health.

THE THREE HUMORS

In Ayurveda three basic constitutional types (or humors)
are recognized. These basic types combine to make seven
possibilities. These seven possibilities vary according to
the degree that they function in an individual.

It is said that our constitution is fixed at the moment
of conception. Both the cosmic humor of the moment (i.e.,
time of day and season) and the dominant humor in each
parent determine the child's constitution. The physical
constitution remains fixed for life, but it is possible to
change the quality of your mental constitution through
spiritual practices. These practices work on the three qual-

ities, or gunas, that pervade the manifestation. Ayurvedic psychology works to balance these three qualities (see chapter 13).

The best way to view the different humors is by seeing each of them as a principle, force, or milieu that helps create an internal environment, and thus a biological being. These three basic principles of prana—the humors—are in constant play with each other. The balance in that interaction determines your level of health. Your ability to maintain that balance determines the length of your life. In Sanskrit these forces are named and imply a multitude of meanings. I have heard it said that every word in Sanskrit has at least four meanings. Thus it is important to recognize that these terms indicate a principle of the life-force. They are not literal translations of the words "air, fire, and water." I will use the traditional Indian names: vata, pitta, and kapha.

Historically, it is said that one must study the three humors for at least seven years in order to fully understand their total significance. They imply the whole of physical manifestation, and are derived from the five states of material existence. See Table 1, p. 28. As you can see from Table 1, motion and space = VATA (V); heat and fluid = PITTA (P); and fluid and solid = KAPHA (K).

Prior to 300 B.C. the Chinese system of medicine used the dualistic concept of Yin and Yang. Along with acupuncture, the Chinese adopted the Five Element Theory which now forms the basis for understanding both Ayurveda and certain branches of Chinese medicine. The five elements are not a simplistic way of dividing the universe. It is actually more correct to call the five elements the five states of matter. They are mass, liquidity, conversion, propulsion, and the field in which they operate. These five states are activated by energy or the given constituent. The concept of a given constituent—energy—was understood by both Chinese and Indian sages. It was called Qi or Prana.

It is only in the last hundred years that certain branches of science have concluded that energy is matter and that matter is energy. The Five Element Theory explains that the given constituent—energy—is the cause of

Table 1. The Five States of Material Existence.

5 ELEMENTS	MANIFESTATION	NATURE	ACTION	→ HUMOR (DOSHA)
Ether =	Space =	Etheric =	Field	
Air =	Motion =	Gaseous =	Propulsion	= V = Dry, Propulsion
Fire =	Energy =	Heat =	Conversion	= P = Hot, Conversion
Water =	Cohesion =	Fluid =	Liquidity	= K = Cool, Cohesion
Earth =	Mass =	Solid =	Density	

the five principles of creation. Energy interacting with the "field" creates movement, or "propulsion"; propulsion creates friction or heat, which causes the "conversion" of energy; conversion causes condensation or "liquidity"; as liquidity settles, "mass" is formed. This acute perception of the universe is the foundation of Ayurvedic medicine.

Dr. Frank Ros gives us a key to understanding the role of prana in the three humors. He points out that Vata is really ether + air + prana; that Pitta is really fire + water + prana; and that Kapha is really water + earth + prana. He states the obvious—which of course is not obvious to normal persons—that prana being life, the animator, the bio-energy, it must be present in each humor.[1] This gives us the clear perception of how acupuncture and pranic healing can balance the three humors by direct manipulation of the pranic currents.

Dr. Robert Svoboda, in his book *Prakruti: Your Ayurvedic Constitution,* gives us yet another way to perceive these three humors as biological principles: water and earth do not naturally stay mixed together; some energy or force is needed to keep them together; kapha is that force. Water and fire do not mix; one will extinguish the other unless, like acid (which is both fire and water), some force can keep them together; pitta is that force. Air needs space in which to move, too much or too little space creates problems, dispersion, or constriction: vata is that force that balances these two.[2] Thus vata, pitta, and kapha are the pranic forces that keep the five states of matter in check and balance.

With this way of looking at the three primary principles, or humors, we can begin to see why traditional Ayurveda says these humors, by their very nature, go out of balance. They are said to be the cause of disease. Dr.

---

[1]Dr. Frank Ros, *The Lost Secrets of Ayurvedic Acupuncture* (Twin Lakes, WI: Lotus Press, 1994), p. 17.

[2]Robert Svoboda, *Prakruti: Your Ayurvedic Constitution* (Albuquerque, NM: Geocom, 1989; Delhi, India: Motilal Banarsidass, 1994), pp. 17-18.

Svoboda gives the translation of the Sanskrit word *dosha* ("humor") as "things which can go out of whack."[3] This is because they have a difficult job keeping solid and fluid, fluid and heat, motion and space functioning smoothly together.

WWWWWaaaiitt a minute! This is a bit complex, what do all these states of matter and principles have to do with me and getting healthy? What do I care if motion and space have a hard time together?

What is muscle pain? It is the restriction of motion by the lack of space. Pain happens to me often due to the deformation of my spine. The physical contraction of the muscles in my back is often caused by overwork: the spine doesn't support my body, the muscles take the load, I begin to feel tension, and then I feel pain. This condition can also be understood as a decrease of space, or flexibility, or relaxation, in my back. Once the space decreases, the energy that moves the muscles gets constricted or blocked and I feel that blockage as pain.

Many of our diseases, aches, and pains can be seen as conflicts between different states of matter. Learning how to harmonize these three humors eliminates the problem from a basic source. Controlling the dominant humor, or the unbalanced humor, results in harmony to the five states of matter, which are the basis of all manifestation, and which include both good health and disease.

Once a great sage was asked by his students what would happen to him at death. He responded: "Where can I go? I am always here." Then he expounded further by saying, "At the death of the body the five elements dissolve back into their sources; earth goes back into earth, water into water, fire into fire, air into air, and space into space."

Briefly, the principle of vata can be described as that which moves everything in the body, including pitta and kapha. It is called the most important humor and is most often out of balance. It is usually the most difficult to cor-

---

[3]Dr. Robert Svoboda, Prakruti: *Your Ayurvedic Constitution,* p. 17.

rect. It is centered in the colon and is responsible for all evacuations of waste from the body.

The principle of pitta can be described as that which transforms everything in the body; it is the metabolic process. Food becomes energy, and information becomes knowledge. Pitta balances the other two humors, for they are opposites of each other. Digestion is controlled by pitta, and it is said that pitta is centered in the small intestines.

The principle of kapha can be described as that which provides the base for the other two humors. It is stability; it provides cohesion in the body. This is reflected as plasma, tissue, muscles; it is centered in the stomach; it controls the liquid in the body.

We are a mix of each of these three forces. One or two will usually predominate, but whatever humor ,is predominant is said to be our constitutional type. If two are equally predominant, then we are said to be of a mixed constitution. The equally balanced constitution of all three humors is said to be rare, but the best for good health and long life. Here are the seven possibilities:

Vata	Vata + Pitta	Vata + Pitta + Kapha
Pitta	Vata + Kapha	
Kapha	Pitta + Kapha	

Some modern practitioners say that there are ten possibilities by indicating the first humor as slightly stronger. For example, PV would indicate that pitta was stronger than vata, and VP would indicate the reverse. This can be useful. The understanding of these principles is the very heart of Ayurveda. There are similarities to other systems in many aspects of Ayurvedic medicine; however, the use of these three humors to diagnose, treat, live, and heal are unique to the Ayurvedic system.

Dr. David Frawley draws the very helpful analogy between the traditional Chinese view and the Ayurvedic constitution in Michael Tierra's book, *Planetary Herbology*. He states that a correlation can be drawn like this:

Yin = Kapha, Yang = Pitta, Qi = Vata.[4]

This correlation was very valuable to me because it enabled me to use certain Chinese medicines to heal myself. It also gave me a much deeper insight into the traditional Chinese medical system.

BEGINNINGS

Let's look at how this system came into existence. This understanding really helps us absorb it on a deeper level.

The sages who developed Ayurveda observed nature very closely. Through the power of detailed observation they came to understand the basic forces of creation: solid matter, liquid matter, radiant energy, gaseous substance, and the space or field in which they are manifested. These forces create three basic forms of energy: propulsion, conversion and cohesion. They were worshipped as the gods Vayu (propulsion), Agni (conversion), and Soma (cohesion).

After observing these principles of nature in the exterior manifestation, the principles were applied to the functions of the human body. The qualities that these forces represent in nature work the same in the body. For example, the force of propulsion manifests as wind in the environment. Wind has the quality of movement, drying, agitation, and cooling. In the body, vata has the same functions: it corresponds to breathing, muscle action, the movement of food through the intestines, and the expulsion of wastes. It has a cooling effect on the body, and creates agitation in the mind when aggravated.

By watching these basic forms of energy in the environment we can learn how to recognize them in ourselves. Think of the sun. What are its qualities? Radiant heat, light, energy, transformation of fuel and our general source of life. In our bodies, we can perceive pitta as the

---

[4]Michael Tierra, *Planetary Herbology* (Twin Lakes, WI: Lotus Press, 1988), p. 427.

metabolism that controls our heat, our eyes sense light, our digestion transforms food, and the metabolic process extracts energy from the nutrients of our food.

As kapha relates to liquid and cohesion, so the water element in our bodies represents the majority of physical matter. Kapha corresponds to the qualities that unite the total organism. It provides lubrication; just as dry dirt crumbles in our hands, the addition of water provides the property of cohesion. Kapha also provides the cooling necessary to balance the fire of pitta and stabilizes our emotions and relationships.

Without any instruments except intelligent observation and profound meditation, the sages were able to accurately describe the functions of the body. Their ability to penetrate our nature through deep meditation gave us profound observations that we are very hard-pressed to match today. It is even more amazing that their system continues to work well thousands of years later.

PHYSICAL CONSTITUTION

It is possible to have a physical constitution different from your mental constitution, but it is unusual in classical Ayurveda. Currently there are several views on the subject. The classical view states that mental and physical constitutions are generally the same. Additionally, classical Ayurveda states that most people are of one constitution, and only a minority have mixed constitutions.

We now view the constitutions differently because of changes brought about by our modern industrialized society. The change is the result of social transformation: we were once part of a fixed social class and family tradition, and now we are a highly mobile culture. Not only does modern culture physically move around more than ever before, it also is blending many more cultures and classes together to form more broad social classes. In other words things are not as fixed or rigid as in the past. This has lead to many more constitutions of a "mixed" or dual nature. This can manifest as a difference between the mental

and physical constitution. My own clinical experience veri-
fies these findings. What may have been classified as a
"pitta" constitution with vata as second or disturbed, may
now be called pitta/vata—a dual type.

The mental always predominates over the physical. I
find the Ayurvedic classifications of the physical body to be
the least helpful in the determination of the constitution. I
give them here because any thesis on Ayurveda would be
incomplete without them. However, I find pulse diagnosis,
observation, the tongue, and verbal interrogation a far
more accurate means of determining a person's constitution. Even better are the mental habits that, when observed carefully, show clearly the over-all constitutional
tendencies.

Jyotish (the science of light), or Vedic astrology, gives
a very profound vision of the mental constitution, and was
traditionally used by all Ayurvedic practitioners in ancient
times. A complete treatment requires that the whole being
be addressed, and Jyotish provides the best overview of an
incarnation. It also provides insights into difficult periods
of health, so that prevention, treatment, and possible
causes can be considered. My personal study of Jyotish
has deepened my understanding of Ayurveda. The indications given below are to be used in the context of your
racial background. Do not compare yourself to another
racially different group of persons.

The Physical Traits

Vata—V people are the thinnest of the three humors.
They tend to have thin bones and a thin body. They tend to
have dry skin and hair; the main quality of vata is DRY.
Physical irregularities are also a sign of V. The erratic behavior of V manifests in all physical irregularities, such as
scoliosis, the deformation of the spine that I have. V people tend to have poor stamina. People who are tall or short
tend to be V. They may have joints that crack (dry) or the
joints protrude a bit from the skin. Their faces may be
asymmetrical, maybe you see a crooked nose or big ears.

Figure 2. Vata body type.

The hair color tends to be dark and the hair has a coarse texture. Usually the hair is wavy or curly (see figure 2).

Pitta—P people are of average build, height, and weight. They tend to be strong, with good stamina and endurance. Physically speaking, P people are hot-blooded (watch out vata and kapha). They are generally the most balanced physically, and tend to have lighter colored hair, fairer

Figure 3. Pitta body type.

skin, and blue or green eyes. They often have a flushed complexion, freckles, or acne. The main quality of pitta is HOT (see figure 3).

Kapha—K people often say that they are pitta. Funny isn't it? A friend of mind brought a book from the USA to me while I was in India. In it there was a test on how to determine your constitution. She was obviously a K body type; you know, a little extra padding, but sure enough, she marked all the body stuff as being P. Is this typical? Well, I've seen it many times since; there might be something to it. Everyone likes to think that they are average so they often mark pitta; this is the disadvantage of going only by the physical looks. After all everyone is average to themselves.

The quality of kapha is HEAVY. Now heavy is relative; relative to V and P they are heavy. Now notice that I don't say fat. If you are carrying a little extra padding then you are probably a K type, but you don't need to be fat to be a kapha person. That is what freaked out my friend, she thought that heavy meant overweight. K people are big, not necessarily fat or overweight. And big means for your frame; you can be short and be solid. If however, you know someone who is big and fat then look no further for a pure K type. K people are the strongest physically, and they have the best endurance and stamina. They generally have brown or black hair. It tends to be slightly oily, and has good luster. They generally have nice skin and pale complexions. They are strong, and when motivated they work hard and steady (see figure 4 on page 38).

MENTAL CONSTITUTION

VATA—"Wait, I'll be right with you," and a few minutes later, "I'm just so busy, where did I put that file? Be right with you. Uh, now what did you want? Oh, just a minute, I just remembered today is the 70th anniversary of the Titanic sinking." The wind just blew through.

Thoughts have a tendency to pass quickly through the mind of the V person. Notorious for erratic behavior, the V person thinks quickly and moves fast from subject to subject. The "air-head" mentioned above is typical of a disorganized V type—always busy, but with little result. This type is forever losing things, misplacing important papers, hiding them in a "safe" place only to forget where the safe place was!

Figure 4. Kapha body type.

The V type has great ability to formulate ideas, surpassing the other types for creativity. Artists, theoretical engineers, philosophers, musicians, and all people who need to think in the abstract are usually strong V people. Usually this type is not so good at following through with ideas once they are conceived. The V type is brilliant when handling immediate problems, and comprehension.

When the V person is out of balance, fear, anxiety, agitation, worry, nervousness, and tension predominate in the mind. In the extreme it can be debilitating. Normally these emotions just accumulate until a V-disease is created—all nervous disorders are classic examples. Constant change aggravates these emotions. A stable, loving home life counters the negative sides of these emotions.

Overindulge? That's my middle name, Mr. Overindulgence himself. V people love to overdo everything; you name it, they overdo it. Whether it is relationships, sex, food binges, drugs (like coffee), alcohol, travel (movement), extreme sports, fast sports, and just about anything that you can get a rush on. Wow! What's left in life? Right, we are living in a predominantly V culture. We are addicted to experience, all experiences, any experiences, just give me a GREAT experience and I'm happy.

All of our indulgences aggravate the V humor, causing the V-related diseases. Because our society loves to indulge, most of us tend to have some imbalance of V. All of our technology tends to disturb the V principle, such as— hold on to your computer boys and girls—movies, videos, and any other sensory input other than Yogi Bear coffee cups. So, what are we supposed to do? Read comic books all the time? Definitely not!

Vata is imbalanced due to the fact that prana, which directly controls vata, is responsible for the functioning of the five senses. Prana gives all the senses the power to function. Without prana the senses lack the ability to sense anything. This means that an over-stimulation of the senses directly affects the five pranas in the body. As stated in chapter 1, the five pranas control all functions of the body. Therefore, meditation is one of the best preventive measures in today's culture because it calms vata and thus the five pranas.

Consistency, schedules, emotional stability, meditation, and love are the best mental medicines for V. The V person can get away with many physical abuses if he or she keeps the mental constitution balanced. No one said we had to be perfect, but we do need to be intelligent. Ayurveda gives us the knowledge to live intelligently.

PITTA—"Hurry up, don't you understand a simple fact? Get out of my way nerd. I'll win no matter what!" The sun is hot and so are the mental attributes associated with the P constitution. Because the P people have very good minds they often understand things more quickly than other constitutions. This often leads to impatience.

The hot or fiery emotions characteristic of P include: anger, impatience, jealousy, and irritability. P people also tend to be critical, perceptive, and intelligent. Their ability to follow through with projects or plans, and their desire to achieve, can put them in roles of responsibility—in either self-employed or executive positions.

Negative P people are extremely difficult. They are dominating, controlling and authoritative. They will sell their own mother for gain—usually not monetary—but for power or control. Very successful people—in business, in politics, or in relationships—are often P types. They like to be in front with all the power and recognition that go with that position.

In their positive or higher developed sense, P people are able to discriminate between true and false issues and people. They have the ability to assimilate knowledge and can apply it to different situations. If not repressed by circumstances, they can produce great quantities of work. However, P people are always followed by their shadow—anger.

P people can get angry at just about anything; I know, I'm one. To use this energy constructively is the challenge of the P person. We always need a project or something to occupy our abundance of energy. Whatever our interests are, it is important to pour ourselves into it totally. The excessive build up of heat or energy—if not used creatively—will explode in anger on those around a P person.

KAPHA—"I'll do it later, where is the chocolate? Come and give me a hug before you start that, what's the hurry?" The archetype of the motherly figure fits well with the K constitution. Security and comfort are high up on the list of K people. They tend to enjoy the securities of family life and all the things associated with it. They are laid back, seldom in a hurry—except to eat—and like to take life slow without stress.

K people don't really like trouble of any kind, especially emotional. They often have difficulty communicating their feelings, and end up suppressing them. Dealing with problems can end up causing food cravings or emotional dependency on others. Usually K people will go out of their way to avoid trouble, even to the extent of eating themselves to death. Food represents comfort and security. Without food, it is hard to have either comfort or security. Therefore, food has a special attraction to K types.

With respect to negative emotions, K people have to watch out for greed, possessiveness, depression, grief, and lethargy. Because of K's desire for creature comforts, greed can be one of their downfalls. They do have the ability to live well, and often—when driven—will become obsessed with making money. Money becomes God. While pitta-people will work for fame and power, K people will work for money alone. They will treat their spouses in the same way as any other possession, not because of control issues, but for security, or to "own" or possess.

Depression can often be the bedfellow of the K person. (It's better to have single beds in that case!) The high level of emotional energy—unless used creatively—can be destructive. The challenge of K types is to use their emotional power to love and care for others and themselves. It is important for K people to live comfortable and secure lives. However, they must be alert not to place too much emphasis on the material, but instead focus on providing a loving, secure environment for their loved ones.

Professionally the K type makes a good manager of anything. Precise and accurate, the K type is thorough and hard working. If you want something done well for a long period of time, the K person is the one you want. The V person can formulate the idea, the P person can implement and control it, but the K person should manage the day-to-day affairs.

In days gone by, the kapha type of mentality pervaded the world as the underlying basis of society. Due to many reasons this has now changed to a predominantly vata mentality. "Be the first one on your block to own. . . . Never before tried by anyone (even your neighbors). . . . The latest method guaranteed to. . . ." Behold, the age of vata!

The advance of mechanical technology, the deterioration of the family unit, mass media, advertising, and the

global emphases on the individual have directly con-
tributed to the domination of the erratic vata mentality in
the world today. It is true that cultures other than North
America and Europe are less vata oriented. However, it is
only a matter of degree. I have traveled much of the world
and find this shift in the world mentality complete and
thorough. This is generally referred to as "Westerniza-
tion." Whatever the term implies, the result is that many
vata diseases are predominating our cultures.

In less "Westernized" cultures, where vata is not as
predominant as in the West, a different phenomenon is
happening. The primary principle in Asia was kapha for
thousands and thousands of years, and as the global shift
to vata happens the old kapha mentality is being aggravated by vata to a negative extreme. Greed is a predominant emotion emerging in many of the new middle classes
in Asia. In the Middle East, the principle of pitta has dominated for ages, and that is now being aggravated by vata.
South America is slowly becoming a vata-predominant culture as it follows North America and Europe.

In the West we are obsessed with any new experience.
Our senses are so overwhelmed, embattled, that the most
violent or obscene movies have little affect on us. The rise
in life-threatening activities—like sex, sports, drugs—
illustrates the demand for "another rush." This is resulting in instability—instability in government, family, society, and in the mind. The complete lack of respect for life
that the erratic movement of aggravated vata creates is
having devastating effects on the young. Already "burned
out" at 16, the lack of cohesion or love in our "Western"
world is causing a tremendous rise in teen suicide and
crime. These are only some of the many signs of a vata
culture.

All of this is the negative or destructive aspect of
prana. When prana, our very life force, is over-stimulated
and aggravated, many side effects take place in the body—
primarily mental instability. This mental aggravation
leads to conflicts on every level of life and eliminates peace
from life. Culturally, over-stimulated prana results in a

lack of respect for life, both toward other humans and our environment.

The answer lies not in going back to some other past culture or time, but rather in understanding. Through the right use of anything harmony can be achieved. Nothing is good or bad in itself, the use determines the result. Ayurveda provides the methods we can use to first understand ourselves and then our world, in order to bring back that harmony which all living beings need. First, starting with ourselves, then with our family, we can balance the three basic principles that create our universe—movement, transformation, and cohesion. The ancient sages perceived them as life, light, and love.

4
What Constitutional Type Are You?

❋ The great sage Vasistha said in gentle accents,
"Fetch water from all the holiest places." And then he
enumerated by name all kinds of auspicious objects—
herbs, roots, flowers, fruits, and leaves. ❋

The following test will help you clarify the descriptions provided in chapter 3. While taking the test remain as objective as possible. Mark what is closest to you on the average, not what may be happening now. For example, after having the flu for a week your weight may be low; mark your normal weight and not your depleted weight after being sick. This test is based on many different sources of information.

All the references to color are to be used to describe your racial tones. If you are Japanese, red would mean redder than your family, not Woody Allen. The same applies to all the body references. If you are a seven-foot-tall Zulu, you must use other Zulus as your reference, not an Eskimo.

Put a circle around either V, P, or K; do not choose two. Mark only one choice for each subject. If you cannot decide what to mark because they all seem right or wrong, then mark "V" for Vata. V people are indecisive. Good Luck!

Constitutional Test

V = VATA; P = PITTA; K = KAPHA	
Childhood V - Thin. P - Medium. K - Plump or chunky.	**Head** V - Small. P - Medium. K - Large.
Body V - Tall or short, thin, poor physique. P - Medium physique. K - Stout, well-developed physique.	**Forehead** V - Small. P - Medium, lines. K - Large.
Weight V - Low, hard to gain, easy to lose. P - Moderate, good muscles, gains evenly. K- Heavy, obese, easy to gain, hard to lose.	**Eyebrows** V - Small, thin. P - Moderate. K - Thick, bushy. **Eyelashes** V - Short, dry. P - Thin, fine. K - Large, thick.
Complexion V - Dull, brown, tans without burning. P - Flushed, fair, pinkish, sunburns easily. K - White, pale, tans evenly with little burning.	**Eyes** V - Large or small, dry, dart around. P - Average, thin, red easily, piercing. K - Wide, white, moist, steady, calm.
Skin V - Dry, cold, rough, cracked. P - Warm, moist, pink, freckles, acne. K - White, moist, cool, soft.	**Nose** V - Thin, small, crooked. P - Medium. K - Wide.
Hair V - Coarse, dry,wavy, wiry. P - Fine, light colors,early gray or bald. K - Abundant, oily, lustrous.	**Lips** V - Large or small, unbalanced top or bottom lip. P - Medium, red, cold sores. K - Moist, full even lips.

Constitutional Test

V = VATA; P = PITTA; K = KAPHA	
Teeth V - Irregular in size, crooked. P - Medium, even K - Even, large, white.	**Feet** V - Dry, rough, cracks. P - Medium, soft, pink. K - Large, firm.
Gums V - Receding gums, brown. P - Bleeding gums, red. K - Pink, good.	**Joints** V - Tend to crack. P - Average size. K - Well built, well-lubricated.
Tongue V - Coated with grayish pink film. P - Coated with yellowish, green film. K- Coated with white film.	**Nails** V - Thin, hard, brittle. P - Soft, pink, rubbery. K - Strong, smooth, pale, thick.
Shoulders V - Thin, small. P - Medium. K - Broad, thick, strong.	**Urine** V - Scanty, colorless, often difficult. P - Profuse, yellow or red, often burning. K - Moderate, white or milky.
Chest V - Twiggy, Charlie Chaplin. P - Sharon Stone, Harrison Ford. K - Pamela Anderson, Arnold Schwarzenegger.	**Feces** V - Scanty, dry, hard, often has gas, constipation. P - Abundant, loose, often burning, diarrhea. K - Moderate, solid, often has mucus in stool.
Arms V - Thin (Charlie). P - Medium (Harrison). K - Large, well-developed (Arnold).	
Hands V - Small, dry, cold, rough. P - Medium, warm, pink. K - Large, thick, moist, cool,firm	**Sweat** V - Little, odorless. P - Profuse, strong smell, K - Moderate, pleasant smell.
Legs V - Small, hard. P - Medium, soft. K - Round, firm.	**Appetite** V - Variable, needs frequent meals. P - Strong, enjoys food, irritable if meal is missed. K - Constant, emotional eaters.

Constitutional Test

V = VATA; P = PITTA; K = KAPHA	

Snacks
V - Likes crunchy snacks.
P - Likes cold drinks and snacks.
K - Likes sweets and creamy snacks.
	Emotions
	V - Anxious, nervous, change-
	    able, creative.
	P - Anger, irritable, jealous.
	K - Attached, sentimental, de-
	    pressed.

Temperature V - Cold, irregular. P - Hot. K - Constantly cool.	**Faith** V - Changeable, rebel. P - Determined, leader. K - Loyal, conservative.

Digestion
V - Irregular.
P - Strong, rapid.
K- Slow, steady.
	Sleep
	V - Light, tends toward insomnia,
	    grinds teeth,
	P - Moderate, bad if troubled
	K - Heavy, difficult to wake up,
	    sleeps easily

Voice V - Low, weak, hoarse, cracks. P - Medium, clear. K - Deep, pleasant.	**Dreams** V - Flying, moving, nightmares P - Colourful, passionate, conflicts. K- Romantic, uneventful, few dreams.

Speech
V - Quick, talkative.
P - Argumentative, convincing,
    likes debate.
K - Slow, deliberate.
	Activity
	V - Quick, erratic, restless.
	P - Motivated, purposeful, goal
	    oriented.
	K - Slow, steady

Mental
V - Quick, adaptable, indecisive,
    loves to theorize.
P - Intelligent, critical, planners,
    idealistic.
K - Slow, steady, tolerant.
	Cliamte
	V - Likes sun and warmth, ner-
	    vous in wind.
	P - Likes cool weather, irritable
	    in high heat.
	K - Likes warmth, suffers in cool
	    damp or humidity

Memory V - Quick, poor long term. P - Clear. K - Slow, good long term.	

Constitutional Test

V= VATA; P= PITTA; K= KAPHA	
Sensitivity V- Noise, pain, cold, drafts. P- Heat, light, color. k- Touch, cold, emotions.	Sexuality V- Irregular, fantasies. P- Strong desire, controlling, angry if unfulfilled. K- Steady, devoted.

Habits
V- Movement, traveling, fun,en-
   tertainment.
P- Sports, politics, activities.
K- Water sports, gardening,
   business.
	Immunity
	V- Variable, low.
	P- Moderate, subject to infec-
	   tions.
	K- Strong.

Endurance V- Low, starts and stops quickly. P- Medium. K- Strong, slow starter.	Finances V- Spends freely. P- Budgets, champagne taste. K- Saves, spends emotionally.

Menses
V- Irregular, scanty flow, dark
   discharge.
P- Regular, intense flow, bright
   discharge
K- Regular, average flow, pale
   discharge.	

When you have finished the test, count how many V's, P's and K's you have. Whatever you have the most of, that is your constitution. Note that there are more questions about your physical body than about your mental constiu- tion. This will give you an idea of the overall type that you are. By now your mental patterns should be clear. If you feel that you are actually two types together, it is okay; it means that you are a dual type.

Keep in mind that we all have different traits. The best way to use this test is to determine the strongest traits in our day-to-day life. Everyone loves something or someone, and where that love is placed gives a clue to our constitution. A vata-person may love art for its creativity, a pitta-person may love art as an expert, wanting to know everything about it, or a kapha-person may love art to collect as a valuable object. In this example the subject, art or beauty, is not the question; the approach toward the subject is in question. It is the approach that gives the mental constitution.

Example
All the counts are in! Out of the 46 possibilities (for men, 47 for women) I have the following results:

$$V = 12 \quad P = 31 \quad K = 3$$

It looks like I am a pitta person, what a surprise! Vata is running a late second, with kapha tailing along at last place.
What does it mean? Well I am what I am! I will be prone to P diseases, P emotions and the P mental traits. What is immediately obvious is that I should cultivate the qualities of the K to balance myself. If I eat an anti-pitta diet, I will avoid many diseases. If I follow an anti-pitta schedule, it will keep me feeling better mentally, physically, and emotionally. And as I already said: cultivate a warm, loving environment that is safe, secure, and comfortable—K environment. It is also very important to develop K-related emotions such as greed—oops! Try again— such as romance, love, patience and understanding.
Let's take another example. A woman came to me who had a K body, not too much overweight and in pretty good health. She came to me to lose weight, but the difficulty was that she had a V mental constitution. That means I could not just give her plants and a diet that are the opposite to K, namely V, or just increase P without addressing vata as well.
The V mentality is erratic and loves to binge. That is really hard on the K body because K is the one who can afford to binge the least. They have slow metabolisms and gain weight just by looking at a cake. V can eat ten pieces

of cake, feel sick, complain and pop! Doesn't gain a gram (sickening isn't it?). The problem in a mixed constitution like this is that V can't discipline itself enough to follow a regular program, like eating three meals a day. V will eat all day on Monday and only once at 11:00 p.m. on Tuesday. This kind of lifestyle jams up K bodies. And once they get jammed up, they get toxic, gain weight, and lose energy.

K needs a regular schedule and stable pattern in the lifestyle. This stability freaks out V, who does not like to be still too long. V then pushes K out for another binge on anything. This just increases the problem further, and whammy, you're sick. People live their whole lives like this, always in conflict with their natural forces.

In the woman mentioned above, I give her a P diet to balance the V and K. I then explained the nature of the these two opposite forces and how they function. Now, when she feels a binge coming on, she can either choose a food that will not aggravate K (such as cherries) or she can do another activity that will satisfy V (such as parachuting or doing something exciting!).

Mixed constitutions are harder to treat than single constitutions because usually they are both aggravated by the time you do something about it. If you can treat them soon enough, then they can be fairly simple.

Mixed constitutions are generally mixed both physically and mentally. Usually your body and mental constitution will be the same. For example, I have a friend who is a V/P mix, which is fairly common in the West. She is a teacher, a P profession and has P traits mentally and physically. However, she also has a high quantity of V. She tends to suffer from nervousness, anxiety, and bites her nails—all V traits. She suffers from hyperacidity in her stomach—a P disorder—if she is too stressed. She is lucky to have a fair amount of K, which aids in balancing her out, especially emotionally. When balanced, she has the best qualities of both, and when stressed, or out of balance, she has the disorders of both.

It is helpful to share this test with a few friends. Talk about the test and get clear on what you are, what your friends are, and start guessing what strangers are just by

observing them. The rest of this book is based on or refers
to your individual constitution, so it is a good idea to understand it pretty well. For further study on this subject
read *Prakruti: Your Ayurvedic Constitution.*[1]

[1]Dr. Robert Svoboda, Prakruti: *Your Ayurvedic Constitution* (Albuquerque,
NM: Geocom, 1989).

5

The Disease Process in the Physical Body

❖ *Ignorance is the root of all ailments from which again arise*
many other torments. Lust is vata and insatiable greed is kapha;
anger is pitta that constantly inflames the breast. ❖

In the course of practicing natural healing, and healing myself of various diseases, I came to understand one of the main differences between natural methods and those of the allopathic, the mechanics' school of medicine. This will be obvious to professionals, but since this book is directed toward the average person, it is worth mentioning.

Natural methods will seldom change your immediate situation in cases of chronic disease. Ayurveda or other natural methods can heal your body and mind with patience and time. However, it is unrealistic to think that after a lifetime of abuse or bad habits, your body will magically be painlessly healed in a few days by taking a couple of herbs. Immediate relief does often occur with Ayurvedic therapies; however, it would be misleading not to state at the beginning of this chapter that it is not the norm. If you want to get a quick fix, you will most probably be disappointed. That doesn't mean that quick fixes are not available in Ayurveda. It means that if your basic attitude toward your health and body is oriented at superficial changes, then you will never really be healthy because the basic cause of illness is not going to be addressed

The basic question here is of self-love. With my clientele, and in my own healing process, this question reoccurred as the key to health. Instead of giving up my responsibility to an outside force—doctor or synthetic medicine—I generated internal power, prana, by deciding to accept and love myself; this leads to healing. Without

this fundamental step natural methods are often power-
less to help our bodies heal. Additionally, understanding
your natural constitution helps in self-acceptance.

In order to heal yourself, it may require a firm decision to change some of the poor habits that are the root
cause of illness. Without self-love, the energy will not be
there to implement those changes. These days most of us
look to someone or something else to give us the energy to
change our destructive habits. Or we take a pill that alle-
viates the need to either take responsibility or get outside
help. The allopathic approach to healing dis-empowers us
as individuals.

This need of wanting our doctors to put us back together again, so we can go and party some more, or smoke
some more, or overeat again is very frustrating for much of
the allopathic community. I have had several long conver-
sations with doctors and their frustration over the prevail-
ing attitudes of patients. This typifies how, as a culture,
we have given away our natural power to care for ourselves, and along with that—self-love. The present situation is unsatisfying for both doctors and patients alike,
and leads to a loveless society. The key to break this cycle
lies with ourselves; health starts with self-love.

Ayurveda offers an alternative to this destructive social pattern. The Ayurvedic practitioner helps each individual to take responsibility again for his or her health
through both lifestyle and dietary changes, along with a
strong emphasis on each person's ultimate need—love.
This quality of love can be generated toward one's self by
prayer, meditation, chanting or many other techniques
that help to harmonize first the prana, and then the mind.
Without mental harmony it is very difficult to love one's
self. In fact, the disturbed mind is the root of self-denial,
destruction, and ultimately bad health.

A few basic changes in our habits will help us reclaim
our own personal power so we can generate self-love and
get healthy. First we must understand the disease process
in the physical body according to Ayurveda.

WHAT IS DISEASE?

According to Ayurveda disease is a result of the three humors becoming out of balance. Remember the literal translation into English of the Sanskrit word dosha (humor) is "that which will go out of balance" or "fault." Traditionally it is said that the imbalance of vata is the primary cause of disease, and therefore the force that disrupts the other two humors. This is due to the inherent instability of prana. The first cause of humoral imbalance (and then disease) is prana. In chapter 1 we described the root causes of pranic disturbances that occur due to mind, vasanas, and ignorance. In this chapter we will see how, once disturbed, the prana starts the destructive process of death or disease.

Pathogenic factors in the body are vata, pitta, and kapha, while those in the mind are rajas and tamas.[2]

Bad habits, a life-style full of stress, tension, repressed emotions, poor diet, overwork, unstable family, devitalized food, and a toxic environment all cause the humors (prana) to go out of balance. In Ayurveda the mental or psychological factors are considered the most important, and the environmental factors are the least important. Like most generalities, this should be looked at with a grain of salt; if you have been working in a nuclear facility for the last ten years, then your environment definitely will have a major impact in the balance of your organism as a whole, even if you have a good mental balance. Provided you don't live on top of, or go to school, or work over a toxic dumping site, then the environmental factors will be less than the mental toxins created through a stressful life-style.

When there is a higher amount of stress or tension, the vata humor (via the prana) is immediately affected.

---

[1]Caraka Samhita, vol. I, R. K. Sharma and Bhagwan Dash, trans. (Varanasi, India: Chowkamba Sanskrit Series Office, 1992), p. 41.

The mental functions have a special relation with this humor; it provides the principle of movement to the body and mind. Mind and prana are inseparable; what affects one affects the other. Because vata provides the movement to the other two humors, its condition is very important for your mental state, which works closely with the prana. This is one of the main reasons why psychological factors are responsible for creating disease.

> This prana is indistinguishably united with the mind. In fact, the consciousness that tends toward thinking, on account of the movement of prana, is known as the mind.[3]

Another view of psychological disturbance can be described as mental toxins. Mental toxins are created by thoughts, which aggravate our emotional and psychological state. If this happens for an hour or a day, the effects pass relatively quickly. If, however, the aggravation lasts for long periods of time, toxins start to accumulate in the intestinal system, the lymphatic system, the organs of purification (liver, spleen, kidneys) and the tissues.

Using this definition of imbalance as according to the three humors, it is evident that all people in modern society must suffer, at one time or another, imbalances in their constitutional makeup. Our current standard of stress and tension in everyday life is commonly accepted as a major cause of disease today. We don't need Ayurveda to know that too much stress kills. What we do need the Ayurvedic system for is to know how to reduce the effects of stress and still live in our society. To better understand how Ayurveda can help us do this, it is necessary to understand the disease process from the Ayurvedic point of view.

---

[2]*Yoga Vasistha: The Supreme Yoga,* vol. I, Swami Venkatesananda, trans. (Shivanandangar, India: The Divine Life Society, 2nd ed. 1991), p. 313.

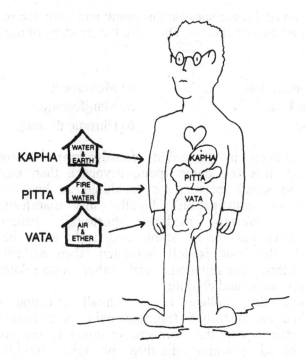

Figure 5. Houses of the three humors.

HOUSES OF THE HUMORS

Each of the humors is said to "live" primarily in one place in the body. This is to be taken both metaphorically and literally because the three humors permeate the entire body, yet the first signs of trouble are usually in the site of their "home" (see figure 5).

> The vata humor lives in the large intestine;
> the pitta humor in the small intestine;
> the kapha humor in the stomach.

Ayurveda states that first a humor will accumulate in its home; then it will become disturbed or aggravated; next it will fill it up or flood the home; then it will move out of its home into the home of another humor, tissue, or organ; the manifestation of disease starts at this point; and lastly the result is a chronic imbalance or disease. These are the six steps of the disease process:

1) Accumulation;   4) Movement
2) Disturbed;   5) Manifestation;
3) Flood   6) Chronic disease.

Vata first collects in the colon (constipation), becomes disturbed (gas), fills the colon (pain, dryness), then moves up either to the small intestine or the lungs or both (variable pain, stiffness, constipation). Finally, this manifests as a "disease" in Western medicine (arthritis); namely the symptoms have become so stable and acute as to be "classifiable." If the root is left untreated, then arthritis, nervous disorders, constipation, and other vata-related diseases become acute and chronic.

Pitta will first collect in the small intestine (hyperacidity), become disturbed (burning pain, acid burps), then it moves either up to the stomach, or down to the colon, or into the blood (burning diarrhea or toxic blood). Next comes the manifestation of disease (ulcers, burning diarrhea, or skin eruptions), and finally its chronic manifestation as a long term problem.

Kapha will first collect in the stomach (bloating, indigestion), become disturbed (nausea, heaviness), then it moves up to the lungs or down to the intestines (coughs, vomiting, mucus). Now comes the manifestation of disease (diabetes, obesity), followed by some chronic illness.

The further along the disease process is, the more difficult it is to cure. It is therefore advisable to pay attention to the small signs of your body rather than ignoring them until they become a manifested illness. Also, the humors will always find the easiest way to move out of their home. This means that if you have a weak knee, vata will move first into that, as vata loves joints. Vata causes muscular pain and cramps as well. In fact, the weak points of your body will always suffer first when one of the humors starts moving out of its home and looks for a weak spot.

MOVEMENT OF DISEASE

Probably one of the most important aspects of Ayurveda is its ability to correct the root imbalance of the organism that is causing the symptoms of disease to appear. The root may not be obvious from our Western point of view. For example, the common cold is a symptom of a high level of toxins in the body, and exhibits the body's ability, or inability, to expel those toxins. Ayurvedically, this it is also an imbalance of kapha flooding the lungs and sinuses. Typically, colds happen during a change of season, when we fail to adapt to the new external forces of nature and continue to eat, dress, and live inappropriately for the new season, thereby creating a higher level of work for the immune system. A cold may be caused by any of the three humors, but will result in aggravating kapha, which will finally flood the upper respiratory system as the immune response is overcome and fails. A cold is a natural function of the body, expelling toxins accumulated through diet and life-style.

Immunity and the immune response system relate to the concept of *ojas*. Ayurveda states that we are born with a certain quantity of ojas for the period of our life, and that if depleted it is very difficult or impossible to replace. The same things that imbalance the humors deplete ojas. Also the use of recreational drugs (alcohol and cigarettes included) and wrong or excessive use of sex will deplete the principle of ojas. There are no moral overtones in these observations, but rather the understanding that if we behave like X then Y will result. Thus, improper or abusive life-styles lower our immunity.

Once any of the three humors becomes imbalanced, it moves into the "three pathways." These are the three major routes that the humors will move through as the disease becomes progressively more severe. An imbalance will start in the first (the inner pathway), move to the second (the outer pathway), then come to rest in the middle pathway.

The inner path relates to the intestinal tract. It is the easiest to cure and the starting place for the majority of diseases. The outer path relates to the skin, blood, and lymphatic, and is more difficult to treat than the inner path. Lastly, we have the middle path, because it is in between the inner and the outer paths. When disease reaches here—the level of inner tissues, bone, marrow, and muscles—it is the hardest to cure. In other words, the illness will start in the intestinal tract, move via the blood to the skin and lymph glands, and then finally work its way into the muscles and bones. Severe diseases involve all the pathways and all the humors.

With this understanding of the disease process we can see why Ayurveda places such importance on the intestinal tract and its health. Normally it is said that the majority of diseases start in the intestines; each humor is also "at home" in the intestinal tract (stomach, small intestine, colon). Food turns to poison in the intestines if it is not digested correctly. This poison results in toxins that aggravate the humors.

Another way to view this approach is to understand what happens to food as it goes through the body. First, food is tasted and chewed. The first taste triggers the appropriate digestive fluids in the mouth and stomach. The food moves to the stomach; if it has been well chewed, then the stomach has an easier time to mix the digestive fluids, liquids, and food together. Once they are mixed together, they move to the small intestine. The small intestine is about twenty feet long. Its work is much easier if the food is well-prepared in the stomach. At the beginning of the small intestine is the duodenum, which is the place where the bile from the liver, gall bladder, and pancreas are mixed together with the food. After this the food moves to the colon, and it is in the colon that the actual value of the food is absorbed—80 percent of the vitamins and nutrients according to Ayurveda. The colon forms the stool and absorbs water from the digested food. It also provides a breeding place for the bacteria that play a beneficial role because of their ability to synthesize important vitamins and absorb nutrients. A normal stool is then passed; it should resemble a ripe banana.

Well, at least that is what is supposed to happen. The real life scenario is more often like this: I quickly half chew a mouthful of devitalized fast food as I wash it down with a soft drink. My sense of taste is confused by the sweet acid taste of the soft drink (which gives two contrary instructions to the stomach) and the burrito I'm eating doesn't have much texture anyway, so I just kind of push it on down.

On reaching the confused stomach, the mixture of cheese and bean burrito, soft drink, and stomach fluids are mixed together. If I have a minute I won't run out immediately, but today I'm busy, so the stomach will have to do its job with half power because I've got to run. It doesn't matter much to me that it takes from three to four hours for the stomach to clear the three burritos and two colas I ate and drank. This disturbs kapha.

About an hour later I'm feeling less heavy in the stomach and start eating chips. Meanwhile, the small intestines don't quite know what to do with these whole kidney beans that slipped through, and even though the liver and pancreas are pumping in the bile, it is not having much effect. My intestine is trying to do a contraction number like the stomach, only it's not as efficient, so it just kind of squeezes things on down the line without waiting for the nutrients to be extracted; after all the chips are already starting to work their way in, too. This disturbs pitta.

Several hours later the colon starts receiving a mass of half-digested kidney beans, which are now starting to ferment rapidly, making a delightful-smelling gas. As the undigested food is now beginning to rot in the colon I am busy eating shrimp curry, rice, and a few beers. Twelve to thirty-six hours later, depending on whether I am a vegetarian and what I've eaten, I will pass out my fast-food lunch. The amount of undigested food will slowly accumulate on the walls of the intestines—large and small—until my body loses the ability to assimilate the nutrients or vitamins. This disrupts vata.

As the undigested food mass accumulates, it starts to pass through the intestinal walls into the blood stream.

The blood stream then carries the toxins (undigested food mass) throughout the body. The immune system then has to work overtime to fight off the toxins as they accumulate in the weaker points of the body. The liver and kidneys also work overtime to filter out the ever-increasing levels of toxins that are escaping from the intestines. When the colon becomes coated with the undigested food, the good bacteria also become overpowered and lose their ability to synthesize the vitamins, thereby adding to the malabsorption of basic nutrients.

After following this scenario, it is easier to understand why Ayurveda says that the toxins resulting from the undigested food mass in the intestines is the underlying cause to most diseases. As these toxins accumulate in the colon, vata becomes aggravated. As these toxins accumulate in the small intestine, pitta becomes aggravated. When the stomach accumulates these toxins, kapha is aggravated. And any of them can move through the blood to aggravate other humors. This movement of toxins through the body aggravates prana or vata.

Therefore, Ayurveda recommends a number of products to increase the digestion of food and to raise the metabolic process in general. With a higher metabolism more heat is created in the body, especially in the digestion process, and toxins can be burned up naturally before they start migration throughout the body with the help of vata. This metabolic heat or process is called *agni* in Ayurveda. Agni is the action of the metabolic process that actually breaks down and transforms food. It is related to pitta because it is fire in nature, but one can have high pitta and low agni. Agni is our ability to actually digest what we eat, while pitta represents the general metabolic process.

Ayurveda also has a complex method to eliminate all toxins from the body and return the humors to their proper home. This therapy is called "the five actions" or *pancha karma*. It is primarily for strong people, neither weak nor very sick. It also requires a few weeks to be effective, often a month is prescribed in order to effectively drive the toxins out of the body. It is a very effective method, but must be administered or supervised by an

Ayurvedic doctor. There are several places in this country where a person can undergo this powerful therapy.

In review, the vata humor, through the unstable nature of prana, is aggravated and is responsible for most diseases. Toxins accumulate in the colon, due to poor digestion and assimilation, causing the accumulation of undigested food. This toxic matter begins to move in different pathways, aggravating the other humors in the process. Thus, it is possible to say that the two primary factors for controlling or preventing the disease process lie in the management of vata and in keeping the intestinal tract free of toxic accumulation by promoting the digestive metabolism (agni). Self-love starts this process by generating the energy or prana needed to implement the changes that create health. Health starts with love, and is maintained by regular digestion and the assimilation of natural foods.

6
The Therapeutic Action of Taste

❖ The priest cooked food of the four kinds and the six different flavors, in accordance with sacred prescription. ❖

To understand how dietary and herbal treatments are used in Ayurveda it is first necessary to understand the Ayurvedic concept of taste. Prana is the source of the five states of matter, which in turn combine to make the six recognized tastes. It is the interaction of the five elements together with prana that give a "taste" to a substance.

> Water and earth constitute the substratum for the manifestation of taste which is the object of the gustatory sense organ. As to the specific qualities of taste, the remaining three (elements: ether, air, fire) are responsible for their manifestation.[1]

Thus we see that the water, then the earth elements are the basis for taste. In fact, without water we cannot taste. Together these two accommodate the possibility for taste, also they provide the basis of most of our food. The other three elements give the qualities to a substance and the variation in taste. Ninety percent of our food has the tastes predominant in the water and earth principles. Together these five elements create the six recognized therapeutic tastes.

---

[1]Caraka Samhita, vol. I, R. K. Sharma and Bhagwan Dash, trans. (Varanasi, India: Chowkamba Sanskrit Series office, 1992), p. 45.

THE SIX TASTES

Taste (and its therapeutic actions) is probably one of the most difficult and foreign concepts for us Westerners to understand. Unfortunately, as a culture we have lost much of our sense of taste due to the overuse of sugar and salt. This is also aided by a lack of the bitter taste which restores the ability to taste and enhances the other tastes. Bitter is the taste most often forgotten, and sugar—well, sugar—what can we say about sugar? Most people overuse it to the point of abuse. Recent studies show that sugar is an immune suppressant. Thirty minutes after taking a total of 100 grams of sugar, in any form, the immune response drops drastically. The effect lasts for five hours. The average American consumes over 110 grams of sugar per day. Salt is almost as abused as sugar. There is a clear distinction between the "taste" and an actual substance. When Ayurveda uses the word "taste," it literally means when you put something on your tongue.

Take for example that American institution—the veggie burger! The basic burger is made of tofu and/or whole grains. This provides a combination of bland, sweet, and slightly oily taste. Now add some salt—they forgot to cook with it (uuggggg!). Now add a few sour pickles (no sweet relish for!), then a hot mustard and some green lettuce. We are almost there—we only need one more ingredient—rhubarb. Rhubarb! OK, I admit I'm hard pressed for the last taste, but it could be a hit: "The Rhubarb Burger" or "The Big R." Wait, this is very profound information (see figure 6 on page 67).

Ayurveda states that there are six basic tastes, and guess what? My "Big R" has them all! Here's the bottom line: if you don't get these six tastes, then your body is deprived of valuable nutrients, minerals, vitamins, and your digestive system will not function correctly. Without all six tastes, the digestion cannot absorb the elements and nutrients that are needed to live disease free. When a disease is present, you can use more of certain tastes to balance out the body. Now my "Big R" doesn't seem so funny does it—taste aside. Here are the six tastes:

Sweet or bland;
Salty or salty;
Sour or acidic;
Pungent or hot;
Bitter or tart;
Astringent.

In the example I gave, the veggie burger and bun give the sweet taste. The salt gives the salty taste. The pickles give the sour taste. The mustard gives the hot taste. The green lettuce gives the astringent taste. And last and not least, the rhubarb gives the bitter taste.

OK, I could have used turmeric for the bitter taste, but who wants a yellow veggie burger? Of course the burger I describe is real food, not a fast-food burger which is predominantly sweet—sour—salty; nothing to do with the "Big R."

The six tastes are the key to understanding the food and herb therapies of Ayurveda. Their system of tastes gives us a method to choose our food and our medicines systematically for our personal constitution. If we use the right balance of tastes for our constitution, then we will seldom, if ever, fall sick, because by using the tastes

Figure 6. The "Big R."

correctly we keep the three humors in balance. This is not a simplistic method of classifying foods and plants; taste has a very definite biochemical effect on the body.

The tastes balance the humors because they are made from the five states of matter—the five elements—just like the humors. Each taste is made of two of the states of matter, just as the humors are. Each taste has three properties—the taste on your tongue, the immediate action, and the long-term action in your body. Three of the tastes have different long-term effects on the body. The long-term effect is very important when using herbs or food as medicine. Why? Because *over a long period of use, you may start to obtain the opposite effect than when you started.*

Some plants have a fourth effect that is the "Catch 22" effect. In Ayurveda, this fourth effect is referred to as the "special action" of an individual plant. It can be seen that there are many musicians but only one Beethoven or only one Mozart. These composers had a very special gift to give humanity; so, too, certain plants have special gifts for humanity. Not all plants have this special action. There is no systematic way to know what the fourth effect is, one must just learn them. Look at Table 2 to see the qualities of the six tastes.

Table 2. Qualities of the Six Tastes.

TASTE	ELEMENTS OR STATES OF MATTER	POTENCY ATTRIBUTES	LONG-TERM EFFECTS
SWEET	Earth+Water	Cold, Damp, Heavy	Sweet
SOUR	Earth+Fire	Hot, Damp, Heavy	Sour
SALTY	Water+Fire	Hot, Moist, Heavy	Sweet
PUNGENT	Fire+air	Hot, Dry, Light	Pungent
BITTER	Air+Ether	Cold, Dry, Light	Pungent
ASTRINGENT	Air+Earth	Cold, Dry, Light	Pungent

Under potency and attributes there are three possibilities. Heat—hot or cold—refers to the action in digestion. For example, if you eat hot salsa or Tabasco sauce, you will feel a burning in your stomach and may even sweat. This degree of hot varies according to the food and how much fire it has in its nature. Moisture—dry or moist—means it has a lubrication effect or a drying effect. Black pepper is drying and milk is moist. Weight—light or heavy—refers to how your stomach feels after a meal, or how hard a food is to digest. Some foods are obvious and others are not; steak is heavy and salad is light. Common sense isn't it? Who said this was complicated?

Each of the humors is increased by three tastes and decreased by the other three tastes. This is how Ayurveda uses the tastes to balance vata, pitta and kapha. Increase means to make it more or stronger. Generally we don't want to increase what we are already. For example, I am a P type, so I have ample heat already, so much so that I created an ulcer. In order to heal that ulcer I needed to avoid all the hot tastes that increase P and use the other three that decrease P. Opposite tastes generally balance, or lower, what is in excess or aggravated.

From Table 3 it is evident that, being a P person, I want to have sweet, bitter, and astringent tastes predominating in my diet. I still need the other tastes, and will eat them, but I have to watch out that I don't use them too much, or I will activate those hot P emotions and possibly a P disease. In the case of an occurring disease, like an ulcer, I had to completely avoid (for a time) the sour and pungent tastes, and could only take salt in an indirect way.

Table 3. The Humors and Tastes.

HUMOR	INCREASES	DECREASES
VATA	Bitter, Pungent, Astringent	Sweet, Sour, Salt
PITTA	Sour, Salt, Pungent	Sweet, Bitter, Astringent
KAPHA	Sweet, Sour, Salt	Pungent, Bitter, Astringent

For someone who is an overweight K type, the pungent, bitter, and astringent tastes will help reduce fat, but care must be taken to still eat enough simple sweet foods to receive the nutrients necessary to live. Never do anything drastic! It will only shock your body, activate its biological survival instincts, and end up having the opposite effect or worse. The idea is to avoid the tastes in their pure forms and use them in their complex form if they IN-CREASE your humor. If they DECREASE your humor, you can use them in their pure form (Table 4).

One thing to understand clearly is that every food or herb has all the tastes. Sometimes the tastes are latent, meaning you cannot actually taste them. Usually one taste will predominate over the other five, but certain tastes are difficult to find in pure forms, like astringent. Astringent is more often a secondary taste to sweet, such as in grains and some meats. Red meat is predominantly sweet in taste. It builds tissues and is nutritious to the body, but because of the sweet, warm, heavy qualities, it is also heavy to digest, taking almost three days to be digested completely. Fish can be too hot for P types, for whom chicken or turkey are better because of their astringent second taste. Chicken is lighter and digests faster because of the astringent secondary taste and because the long-

Table 4. The Pure and Complex From for Taste.

TASTE	PURE FORM	COMPLEX FORM
SWEET	Sugars	Complex carbohydrates, Grains
SOUR	Alcohol	Yogurt, Lemon
SALT	Table salt	Soy sauce, Seaweed
PUNGENT	Cayenne pepper	Mild spice, Cinnamon, Onions
BITTER	Gentian Aloe	Rhubarb, leafy dark green plants
ASTRINGENT	Unripe bananas	Pomegranates, Cranberries

term effect is pungent, which is the antidote to sweet. However, all meat is tamasic or dulling in quality and is not recommended as a daily food in Yoga or Ayurveda. Virtually all our basic foods are predominantly of the sweet taste.

PHYSICAL EFFECTS OF TASTES

The following list provides the primary effects that each taste has on the body. If you work with Ayurveda, this is a list that you will commit to memory.

SWEET: Is the primary taste for building the body, both in tissue growth and in strengthening the structure. It is soothing in the body and helps harmonize both body and mind. It brings contentment and satisfaction. It helps to increase reproductive fluids; is cooling to the body; commonly found in food, rare in herbs.

Abuse: Overuse of the sweet taste causes obesity, accumulation of toxins, parasites, diabetes, obstructions in the body's channels, gas, indigestion, and lethargy.

SOUR: It is a stimulant to the body, primarily the digestion. It dispels gas, nourishes the body, and builds all tissues except the reproductive tissues. It strengthens the sense organs and causes secretions of fluids in the body; commonly found in foods, rare in herbs.

Abuse: Overuse of the sour taste causes acidity in the small intestine, burning, itching, premature aging, and light-headedness.

SALTY:—It is a stimulant, sedative, and a laxative, depending on the quantities used. It softens the body tissues and retains water in the system; it can nullify the other tastes; not common in food or herbs.

Abuse: Excess causes inflammation, skin diseases, impotence, looseness of body, premature aging, and retention of water.

Table 5. The Six Tastes and Their Values.

TASTE	NUTRITIVE VALUE	MEDICAL VALUE	IN EXCESS CAUSES	ORGAN AFFECTED IN EXCESS
SWEET	Great	Little	Toxins	Pancreas, Spleen
SOUR	Moderate	Little	Acidity	Liver
SALT	Some	Little	Looseness	Kidneys
PUNGENT	Some	Good	Burning	Lungs, Small intestine
BITTER	Least	Great	Cold	Heart
ASTRINGENT	Small	Great	Contract	Colon

PUNGENT: This is the strongest stimulant aiding the digestion and activating the metabolism. It dispels gas and induces sweating. It is heating to the body and cleans the blood and skin; rarely found in foods, commonly found in herbs.

Abuse: Too much pungent taste causes pain, emaciation, burning sensations, fever, thirst, drying of reproductive fluids.

BITTER: The bitter taste is found more in herbs and spices and is the best blood purifier and cleaner of toxins in the body. It promotes all the other tastes. It reduces tissues and fluids, and relieves burning in the body. It is strongly cooling to the body; not commonly found in most foods, very commonly found in herbs.

Abuse: Excess of bitter causes coldness in the body, nervous disorders, stiffness, colic pain, headaches, and the reduction of reproductive fluids.

ASTRINGENT: Is the best at constricting everything in the body. This makes it valuable as a medicine in that it stops bleeding and discharges. It heals the mucus mem-

branes and the skin. In small amounts it aids the digestion of foods; commonly found in both foods and herbs.

Abuse: Overuse of astringent causes dryness of the body,
constipation, cramps, emaciation, thirst, nervous disorders, and decreased reproductive fluids.

Table 5 shows some of the other values of the six tastes.
The degrees stated are relative to each other, great being
the strongest.

EMOTIONAL EFFECTS

The tastes also affect us psychologically. Expressions such
as "a dried up old bag," "he's still bitter after all these
years," "she's a sour puss," "isn't she sweet?," "he has a
sharp tongue," "an old salt," "it left a sour taste in my
mouth," are all familiar to us. All these sayings express
emotional tastes or frames of mind. It is said that the effect of emotional taste is stronger than the taste resulting
from food and herbs. As with all forms of health, our mental attitude plays a decisive role in maintaining and healing ourselves. Sweet represents love, sour represents envy,
salty represents greed, pungent represents anger, bitter
represents grief, and astringent represents fear.

It should be noted that traditionally taste is considered the first and least strong in medical treatments or
therapy. It is generally stated that taste is overcome by
the long-term effect of herbs or food. This in turn is overcome by the action which gives way to the "Catch 22" effect, or the special gift of a plant. We can also understand
"taste" as the pharmacological action of the food or plant
being used.[2] Therefore, taste can be used primarily for our
daily food regimen and herbal supplements, but for medical needs the special action of an herb should be given primary consideration.

---

[2]Brigit Heyn, *Ayuruedic Medicine: The Gentle Strength of Indian Healing*
(New Delhi, India: IndusHarperCollins India, 1992), p. 100.

7

Food and the Three Humors

❖ *Piercing the seven veils of the universe (consisting of earth, water, fire, air, ether, the cosmic ego, and the cosmic intellect), I mounted to the utmost height I could reach; but when I saw the Lord's arms even there, I was again dumbfounded.* ❖

There is no such thing as an Ayurvedic food or an Ayurvedic herb. Nothing is Ayurvedic and yet everything can be used in the Ayurvedic way. Ayurveda is a vision of how to live in harmony with ourselves and our environment, encompassing the full body/mind/spirit relationship with the cosmos. A piece of rhubarb is not an Ayurvedic food; however, it can be used according to Ayurvedic precepts and philosophy to achieve therapeutic results according to the Ayurvedic system. Thus, no food or herb can be called Ayurvedic because Ayurveda is a way of perceiving the world, not an object in the world. There is only the direct observation of interrelated actions: A + B = C. This is Ayurveda.

> The human race has been practicing medicine for many thousands of years and from all available reports, it has been reasonably successful. . . . Where practiced, improved sanitation and proper diet have done more for health than any medicine that has ever been used. Few people seem to manage these conditions in their lives, and so medicines are required to perform a monumental task.[1]

---

[1]Subhuti Dharmananda, Ph.D., Editor's Preface in Michael Tierra, *The Way of Herbs* (New York: Pocket Books, 1980), p. x.

FOOD AS MEDICINE

Food is the best medicine and the best long-term treatment available in any system of medicine anywhere in the world. A balanced diet is critical for good health. Wrong diet is responsible for 90 percent of physical disease. Wrong diet can also reduce or nullify the effects of herbal treatments, therefore Ayurveda places considerable importance on the correct food and the optimum ways to prepare and eat that food.

A balanced diet for Ayurveda can be very different from what we commonly understand in the West. Balance is in reference to the three humors and agni (the digestive ability), not to vitamins, minerals, and nutrients. This is because Ayurveda perceives people as individuals and not machines. The six tastes are used to determine which foods are good for your constitution. First you must determine your individual constitution, then you must know the basic action of the tastes on you—for example, sour, salty, pungent tastes increase pitta, so should be avoided in every meal if you are pitta. Lastly you can choose the foods that balance or harmonize your constitution over a long period of time.

With a machine it is possible to provide a maintenance plan for each model—2 door, 4 door, big, small. But for human beings it is impossible. One person's poison is another person's medicine. This is due to the predominance of different humors. A V person will need very different foods than a K person. All constitutions must adjust their diets according to the seasons. This is especially true for people with mixed constitutions.

The analogy of the car is perfect for many doctors and nutritionists today. They look at people as machines that need different fuel and lubricants to operate smoothly. Why doesn't the mechanical school of diet and medicine work? Well, it does work if it happens to fit your constitution, and it doesn't if you are of another constitution. That's why there are many different dietary methods existing today, because there are so many different constitutional possibilities. Western nutritional theories do not consider that you may digest food and minerals differently from the next person.

While you may be able to run all cars on gasoline and achieve similar results—i.e., it runs—you cannot feed all people on the same food with similar results. Someone may be satisfied with a Chinese meal for four or five hours while another person may be hungry again in two hours. The metabolism of each person is very different and has different needs. The metabolism is the sum total of the three humors, balanced and controlled by pitta and agni.

Food and drink are the most important medicines for the body because they are the most consistently ingested substance in the body. What you drink ultimately turns into prana and what you eat ultimately turns into ojas (ojas is the basis of your reproductive fluids and of the immune system). The best quality gasoline will provide your automobile engine with a longer life, so, too, will the best quality food provide you with a longer life. Ayurveda says that food closest to its natural state provides the best quality and quantity of prana, therefore vitality to the body. Processed foods do not have enough (if any) prana to vitalize the body over a long term; they also produce little or an inferior quality of ojas. That means that buying a fresh head of broccoli at a large supermarket is better than frozen or commercially canned broccoli, but by far the best choice is to buy it from the farmer.

Ayurveda states that food is far easier to digest when lightly cooked. And if it is cooked with a little spice it is even easier to digest. Just think, you have a head of broccoli, fresh from the flock, and you wash and eat it raw. Pretty boring isn't it? Ayurveda thinks so too. They like to cook with a few spices, like cumin and onion, but you could just as well use thyme and rosemary (depending on your constitution). Adding this to a rice dish or lentils, or topping off your pizza with it makes a much more interesting meal.

Ayurvedic cooking is not an endless repetition of curries, and it has little or nothing to do with commercial Indian cooking as experienced in India. If you want to get a quick case a heartburn, ulcers, or just plain old diarrhea, go to India. Unless you are lucky enough to eat at the home of a traditional family, you won't experience Ayurvedic cooking in India. Traditional families will not use chilies, garlic, onion, or other strong spices because it is known to promote aggression and imbalances the mind. (This explains the aggressive assaults by beggars, vendors, and shopkeepers on non-chili eating tourists.)

Yes, it is amazing! You don't need to eat yellow sauces the rest of your life in order to eat according to the Ayurvedic system of plant and food energies. Because as mentioned earlier, there really is no such thing as Ayurvedic food. There is only a system to ascertain the energetic actions of plants and foods. With this system of assessment it is possible to use food from any climate or culture in the Ayurvedic manner. *The correct balance of food energetics for your constitution is the best medicine and the best dietary regime for a long, healthy life*

EXCERPTS FROM THE CARAKA SAMHITA

Chapter twenty-five in the first book of the Caraka Samhita talks only about food. The chapter starts like most of the different sections, with the sages sitting around discussing Ayurvedic precepts. Ayurveda is not static, consequently teaching was in the form of disciples debating with each other and the teacher keeping things on track. This discussion starts out with the King of Kashi (modern day Varanasi, the oldest continually inhabited city in the world) asking if disease arises from the same source as we did or if it arises from some other external influence. After a debate and various views being given the teacher, Atreya tells them all to stop controversial debating as it perpetually goes around truth, but never arrives at it, something like modern politics.

That much being said, the sage goes on to say that the things in life that normally cause good health, when consumed in the wrong combination or the wrong season, cause disease. The King of Kashi then asks the critical question: "Oh! Lord, what are these factors whose wholesome and unwholesome combinations are responsible for the growth of living beings and their diseases. Atreya said, 'wholesome causes the growth of living beings and unwholesome food the growth of disease.' "[2]

Now all the students want to know how to distinguish wholesome food from unwholesome food when there are so many different factors involved. They are: dose, time, preparation, habitat, individual constitution, kind of disease, strength of the person and age. No problem says Atreya, foods that maintain the balance of the seven tissues and the three humors are wholesome, and those that imbalance the humors and tissues are unwholesome. *This is the definition of a good, balanced diet in Ayurveda.* But, hold on says the faithful author, Agnivesa, that is just too simplistic, we need a much more precise method of figuring out all this wholesome and unwholesome stuff. Agnivesa is a little like us, we need real specific guidelines.

The teacher responds by saying that any good doctor can figure this stuff out. (Too bad for us!) His point is that if you know the properties of food—the combinations of the six tastes and their actions—then you will not have trouble knowing what to recommend to patients. He then says that once you understand the basic qualities of food, then the rest must be determined according to each individual situation. However, he also realizes that not every doctor is good, so he starts to give the various properties of the twenty best foods, and also what he considers to be the twenty worst foods for balancing the humors. These twenty items are from twenty different categories of products: grains, beans, water, salt, vegetable, animal, bird, animal who lives in a hole, fish, ghee, milk, vegetable oil, fat of marshy animals, fat of fish, fat of aquatic birds, fat of domestic birds, fat of grazing animals, roots, fruits, and sugar. This is just an example to demonstrate the thorough classifications of Ayurvedic food categories.

---

[2]Caraka Samhita, vol. I, R. K. Sharma and Bhagwan Dash, trans. (Varanasi, India: Chowkamba Sanskrit Series Office, 1992), p. 419.

Vedic culture was predominantly vegetarian in the higher levels of society, nevertheless the ruling and warrior classes would generally eat meat. The poorer classes would eat anything available, as is still the case today. The lowest classes eat the animals that no one else eats, like pork and other foods that Ayurveda considers unwholesome. However, Ayurveda also understood the great nutritive value of animals and animal products. Normally, they used milk, butter, and ghee as the main source of animal proteins, but when the situation demanded, they prescribed animal products to quickly build back the strength of a person.

The whole point here is that by the careful selection of foods according to 1) category, 2) qualities, 3) actions, 4) tastes, 5) long-term effects, and 6) overall effect on the humors, you can either balance or imbalance your body. So, the intelligent person learns either from study or experience, or both, which foods agree with his or her body. I advise my clients to study Amadea Morningstar's two books on Ayurvedic cooking.[3] Her books provide an enormous amount of information on nutrition and Ayurveda as well as recipes for cooking Indian and Western dishes according to Ayurvedic precepts.

EATING

Good nutrition in the Caraka Samhita is eating the right kind of food, with the right beverage, eating the right amount of food, at the right time, with the right company, in the right place, and in the right frame of mind. We have mentioned what is meant by the right food—according to your constitution, in as natural a state as possible, and lightly cooked—now what are the other "rights'?

Some cultures say that it is bad to drink liquids with the meal. This is false; the stomach needs to have liquid in

---

[3] Amadea Morningstar, *The Ayurvedic Cookbook and Ayurvedic Cooking for Westerners* (Twin Lakes, WI: Lotus Press, 1990 and 1994).

order to help soften and lubricate the food coming into it. However, liquid should never be taken very cold or very hot with food. Of the two, cold is more damaging—especially to K people—because it suppresses and dilutes the digestive fluids being secreted by the stomach, pancreas, liver, and gall bladder. Liquid should be sipped with the meal, lubricating the food as you eat. If a large amount of liquid is drunk either before or after a meal, it also slows down or stops the digestion.

It is also incorrect to drink "X" amount of fluid per day. One should drink when thirsty. If there is excessive thirst, it is a message from the body that too much of the pungent or astringent taste is present. It can indicate high amounts of P or aggravated V. Pure water is the best for the body, but may not satisfy V people enough on its own. Then herbal teas should be used as well. Remember, the essence of water becomes the prana in the body. The failure to drink neutral or natural substances directly affects your level of day-to-day energy. All "soft" drinks (What's soft about them? They are very acidic.), coffee, tea, and alcohol are damaging to some extent to the prana and the vata related organs, like the kidneys. If used daily they are very damaging, depleting a person's over-all vitality and immune response.

The sages observed that people live far longer when they eat less quantities of food. The method to determine what is right for you is to eat until your first burp; that's your body's signal to stop. If you eat past that point, you are reducing the length of your life by overworking your system. The correct ratio in the stomach is 1/3 food, 1/3 liquid and 1/3 space. (Note: some schools state 1/2 food, 1/4 liquid and 1/4 space.) The stomach needs the space to perform its job, mixing the food with the digestive secretions. By filling your stomach up all the way, it becomes very difficult for the muscle walls of the stomach to properly contract and expand, thereby limiting the amount of preparation of the food before actual digestion begins in the small intestine.

There are also correct times in the day to eat for each humor. The determination of the times is due to the cycle

Table 6. Times of the Humors

HUMOR	DAY	NIGHT	SEASON
VATA	3 A.M. to 7 A.M.	3 p.m. to 7 p.m.	August to November
PITTA	11 A.M. to 3 p.m	11 p.m. to 3 A.M.	April to August
KAPHA	7 A.M. to 11 A.M	7 p.m. to 11 p.m.	December to April

of the Sun. Each twenty-four hour period is divided into six four-hour divisions. These correspond to the three humors, three in the day and three at night. The divisions are shown in Table 6.

When looking at this kind of traditional information, remember that the sages actually went by the movement of the Sun, not the clock, nor did they use Daylight Savings Time, nor did they consider other modern factors. Look at vata, for example: it is highest during sunrise and sunset. If that corresponds to your area, good; if not, adjust the times. According to Table 6, sunrise would be at about 5 a.m. and sunset is 6-ish. Kapha is highest in the mid-morning and early evening, and pitta is highest at noon and midnight.

These times tell us when we can eat with the least problem for our constitution. K should not eat much or any breakfast—high K time; they will gain weight due to slow digestion. K can eat a big lunch between 11 a.m. and 1 p.m.—this time digestion is at its best. K can eat a light dinner from 5 p.m. to 7 p.m.—near the end of vata time, a light meal will have no bad effects.

P can eat a good breakfast, when digestion is generally its strongest, and kapha time from 7 a.m. to 8 a.m. is not a problem for the hot P person. P should eat a lighter, cooler lunch from 12 noon to 2 p.m. because P is too hot already at this time. P can eat a good dinner from 5 p.m. to 8 p.m., V and K time, for the cooler times enable them to eat spicy food without overheating the body.

It is most important for V to eat regularly. Breakfast can be taken from 6 a.m. to 9 a.m., warm moist foods should be eaten, definitely not dry, cold food—V food. A good lunch can be taken from 12 noon to 2 p.m., the high pitta time. Cool food is tolerable at this time. And a warm, moderate dinner should be taken from 5 p.m. to 7 p.m., also with care not to have cold food again.

No one should eat before sleeping or late at night. The body needs three hours to digest the food before sleeping and at least one hour before engaging in a physical activity like sex or jogging.

Who we eat with is very important. If you don't like someone, how can you expect your food and digestion to like them? It is impossible to separate the functions of the body from our personality and mental functions. If that is done then you arrive back at the 2-door, 4-door model of mechanical medicine. The body/mind/emotions work as a unit. Try this for size: fix a nice dinner, sit down to eat, and after five minutes or so start yelling and screaming at whoever you are eating with. About five minutes should do the trick. Now how does your stomach feel? Good? Is it unaffected by your anger? Try it and see.

Unspoken tension is worse from my experience. I was brought up in a middle class family that was perfect—perfect house, perfect car, Dad had the perfect white collar job, and Mom was the perfect beautiful wife. Only everything was really wrong, terribly wrong, but no one ever spoke about it. Ayurveda tells us that this kind of situation is sending subtle poisons, along with the food, into our body. I have to agree, judging from my family, or rather the extinction of my family that resulted from the accumulation of tensions and emotional poisons.

The place we eat should be aesthetic, clean, and not overly crowded. This is important because it provides a relaxing environment in which to eat and enjoy our food. Even if you are a Quaker and don't believe in enjoying anything, then look sit it from the angle that it is the most efficient for the body—which happens to be the case.

Peace of mind is the most important of all the factors listed above, whether you are a vegetarian or not. The mind or mental atmosphere overrides all other foods, times, and environments. If you are happy when you eat, you are doing the right thing. Have you ever eaten in a macrobiotic restaurant in Paris? There are few tortures that compare to enduring the mental vibrations emanating from the person next to you who is more concerned with chewing his brown rice 500 times than with dealing with his troubled mind. By the way, I like macrobiotic cooking; however, serious, rigid mental perspectives on food (especially while eating) are downright bad for digestion. Please note that while macrobiotic cooking is therapeutic, it is not suited for all constitutions as a basic diet. In addition, chewing your food thoroughly, but not excessively, is excellent for the body, rigid concepts of the mind are not.

DIGESTION

Ayurveda says that each of the three humors contributes to the digestive process. V contributes to movement, and K to lubrication, but the P humor directly controls our ability to digest. According to the precepts of Ayurveda, the external Sun provides life to all the Earth through heat, transformation, light, and unseen energies. The same actions are applied to the P humor (as it is derived from agni, the principle of fire and transformation). It is centered in the small intestine—commonly known for heartburn—provides the heat in the body (metabolism), and is responsible for transforming food into energy. Each cell has the ability to absorb and transform energy like the small intestine, but it is said that each humor resides in the place of its primary action; for the pitta humor that's the small intestine.

There is so much emphasis placed on digestion and the quality of it in Ayurveda that it could be considered obsessive. (My mother certainly thought so a few years ago when she visited me; she said, "All you ever talk about is your digestion!") The importance of digestion cannot be underrated or just passed over briefly. It is wrongly assumed that whatever food you put in you stomach will generally contribute to the nourishment of the body. In actual fact it is what you are able to digest that is important. Few people can digest all they eat; most people have a digestion that is running far below normal due to a weak or suppressed digestive fire.

In Ayurveda there is a difference between the actual ability to digest food and the pitta humor which controls the overall digestion and metabolism. They call this function agni, like the god of fire, but in reference to the body it really means your actual ability to digest something. So a person can have high pitta, but low agni. This was, in fact, my case when I returned from living in India. For the first time in six years of living in India I contracted giardia (intestinal parasites), and after some months amoebas. They both knocked out my agni, or the actual ability to digest the food even after I got rid of the beasts. It was a long process to re-ignite agni; I used a satvic diet (with a little French Bordeaux to even things up!) and the correct digestive herbs.

Perhaps it is interesting to note cultural differences in diet and their relation to the body's ability to digest them. For example, the French eat an enormous amount of dairy products as compared to the Americans, yet as a culture they maintain the digestive enzymes (agni) necessary to process these foods. Americans generally are not able to maintain this kind of diet for any length of time. The French custom of drinking red wine with cheese at the end of a meal is actually following Ayurvedic precepts considering their normal heavy diet. The heating wine (pitta) is a strong digestive agent, helping to process the heavy (kapha) fermented cheese. In France, wine is not alcohol! Alcohol is hard liquor, wine is good for health! Although this is often taken to the extreme, there is both Ayurvedic and scientific evidence to support this view. Bear in mind that this, like all other information, has to be applied to your individual situation and constitution. If you eat a heavy diet, drinking wine may be appropriate; however, if you eat a light satvic vegetarian diet, wine will imbalance you fairly quickly. For wine lovers, please note that older wines aggravate pitta less than younger wines, and that reds are less acidic than whites generally.

In my practice I often find people with low agni, which is usually centered around a malabsorption syndrome. This is primarily the lack of agni in the small intestine, which then allows food to pass though the digestive process without extracting the vitamins and nutrients needed for normal health. This often creates a weight problem because the body feels starved, not because of a lack of food, rather due to a lack of absorption. To correct low agni and the malabsorption syndrome, a pure natural foods diet according to your constitution and the correct digestive herbs are necessary. Ghee is considered excellent for maintaining and promoting agni. Short fasts are usually needed to begin to reeducate the body along with the change in diet and herbs.

The pitta humor exists as acids and enzymes in the digestive tract. The excessive and continual use of heavy, fat foods, junk foods, cold food and drinks, meats, raw foods, and cheese will reduce the quantity and quality of the digestive enzymes in the intestines. If this continues, a mass of undigested foods will start to accumulate on the intestinal walls; this leads to the non-assimilation of the nutrients in your food and low agni.

In summary, it is what our bodies can digest that is important, not how much we eat, although overeating will reduce the overall life span. The daily diet should consist of foods in their natural states, processed foods of any kind are to be avoided. It is far more important to watch what kind of food we put in our minds than what we put in our mouths. My teacher in India once said to us: "People are more concerned with what goes into their mouths than what comes out of their mouths." Hence, a loving attitude toward all beings, especially those with whom we eat, greatly helps the absorption of the vital nutrients and prana in our food.

8

Ayurvedic Herbs

*❖ Devotion to Rama is the life-giving herb, and a mind
full of faith the vehicle in which it is administered.
By this process the diseases will assuredly be healed;
otherwise all our efforts go for nothing. ❖*

Plants and herbs, like everything else, are manifestations
of prana. It is prana that gives everything life, and it is the
prana of each plant that affects our individual pranas to
achieve a therapeutic effect. From a mechanical point of
view, it is the interaction of biochemicals between human
and plant that causes any given therapeutic effect. However, from the subtle Ayurvedic point of view, these mechanical actions are caused by the prana itself. In other
words, it is the prana that gives the power to each chemical, and it is the pranic interaction with a chemical that
starts the biochemical effect. As prana is the force behind
each chemical action, we can also recognize it as the fundamental force acting through plants and herbs.

Prana itself is neutral, having no inherent quality except movement. While motion or movement is the only
quality of prana, its interaction with the other two cosmic
principals of transformation (agni) and cohesion (soma)
impart different qualities to the neutral prana on the most
subtle level. On a more material level, it gains different
qualities through its interaction with the five states of
matter—earth, water, fire, air and ether. Together with
the different material combinations prana imparts different qualities to the plant it inhabits.

> In this universe earth, water, fire, air, and space are each
> of them twice the magnitude of the preceding one. Dis-
> solve the earth in water, water in fire, fire in air, and air

in space. Space should be merged in the cosmic space which is the cause for all. Remaining there for an instant in his subtle body, the yogi should feel that "I am the self of all," having abandoned all self-limitation. That in which this universe rests and which is devoid of name and form is known as prakriti (nature) by some, Maya (illusion) by others and as subatomic by others.[1]

Ayurveda continuously views life as a whole. This view described in the Yoga Vasistha above shows the sages considered that a conscious presence abides in all existence; manifest or unmanifest. Simply put, prana is responsible for our life and is also responsible for the life in all other living beings. By the correct use of other forms of life we can either increase or decrease our own prana or life-force.

> The earth . . . inhales and exhales stellar and cosmic forces. . . . These forces are not all material, but include subtle energies of an occult or spiritual nature. Plants transmit the vital-emotional impulses, the life-force that is hidden in light. That is the gift, the grace, the power of plants.[2]

The six tastes that we talked about in chapter 6 are the combination of prana with the five elements. Herbs follow the same rules that are outlined for food, as herbs are food as well. By applying the rules of the six tastes to our herbal intake we are, in fact, stimulating different pranas that control different actions in the body. Whether we use food or herbs, it is the prana that they carry that creates the therapeutic action in our body.

---

[1] *Yoga Vasistha: The Supreme Yoga, vol.* II, Swami Venkatesananda, trans. (Shivanandanagar, India: The Divine Life Society, 2nd ed., 1991), p. 495.

[2] Dr. David Frawley and Dr. Vasant Lad, *The Yoga of Herbs* (Twin Lakes, WI: Lotus Press, 1986)

THE SIX CLASSIFICATIONS

Ayurveda classifies everything by taste, but marks the difference between foods and medicinal herbs. Foods generally have a therapeutic effect according to their taste, whereas herbs tend to create their primary effect by their potency (heating or cooling action) and their secondary effect by taste.

Traditionally there are six classifications for every substance that we ingest into the body. They are:

English	*Sanskrit*
Taste:	Rasa;
Attribute or quality:	Guna;
Potency:	Virya;
Long-term effect:	Vipaka;
General action:	Karma;
Specific action:	Prabhava.

This is a more profound explanation of Table 2 in chapter 6. This table is necessary for the therapeutic use of herbs, in which all six classifications must be considered. For diet, the simple Table 2 in chapter 6 is sufficient.

Not every substance has all six of these classifications; for example, all have a general action, but may not have a specific action. The traditional classifications are very clearly defined (although there are minor disagreements according to various Ayurvedic schools), and it is with this demarcation that foods and herbs are assigned to people suffering from disease or an imbalance of one of the three humors.

> Vaidya (Doctor) Bhagwan Dash describes the six actions in his translation of a 14th-century Materia Medica: Taste (Rasa) is the result of the combination of the five states of matter or elements. . . . Attributes (Gunas) are divided into ten groups of opposites, such as heavy or light, etc. . . . Potency (Virya) is of two kinds, namely hot or cold and as such they produce heating or cooling effects in the body. . . . Long-term effect (Vipaka) is the post-digestive effect or the action that remains after the metabolic transformation of

the substance. . . . Action (Karma) is the result of the above four actions in combination with the enzymes (both digestive and cellular), together all of these create the General Action of which thirty important ones are given here. . . . Specific Action (Prabhava) is the special action of a substance when ingested by a living being [the Catch 22] .[3]

In addition to the six classifications there is a "therapeutic action" or the action on the three humors. Some herbs are call "tri-doshic," which means that they have a balancing effect on all three humors. Generally these are herbs that have four or five of the six tastes. Other herbs may work on two of the humors, while still others may only work on one. This is the category that relates directly to your individual constitution. For beginners this is the easiest category to start from. If you know your constitution (and if you don't, go back to chapter 4 and figure it out!), then you only need to see how a plant generally affects your constitution to see if it works for you or not. To treat an imbalance with herbs see chapter 14 for the basic methodology of balancing the humors.

I will now list some of the Ayurvedic herbs that are currently available in this country along with their actions according to the Materia Medica of Bhagwan Dash, which has been enlarged with information from *The Yoga of Herbs*. For the Ayurvedic classification of Western herbs, the *Yoga of Herbs* and Michael Tierra's two books are the best references.[4] strongly recommend these books to everyone interested in the Ayurvedic use of plants and herbs.

A word about dosage is needed. Herbs are safe and effective if taken correctly. Rarely some herb—depending on which one—can be unsafe if taken incorrectly. *Always follow the recommended usage.* When an herb is listed as an aphrodisiac, for example, it doesn't mean that one can realize a stronger effect from a huge dose. It does mean that

---

[3]Dr. Bhagwan Dash, *Materia Medica of Ayurveda* (New Delhi, India: B. Jain Publishers, 1991) pps. xxiv-xxxviii

[4]Frawley and Lad, The Yoga of Herbs and Michael Tierra, *The Way of Herbs* (New York: Pocket Books, 1980), and *Planetary Herbology* (Twin Lakes, WI: Press, 1988).

if taken regularly over a period of time the desired effects will be achieved. Long-term usage is the key to herbal supplements and medicines. Sometimes relatively large doses are needed for therapeutic effects to be achieved. However, attention should be paid to the prescribed dose. Herbs function better if other synthetic drugs are not used. This includes all forms of alcohol and caffeine. If a diet consisting of whole foods is taken along with herbs, their effectiveness is greatly increased. Herbs are safe, safer by far than any synthetic drug, but respect must be given to the correct dosage.

Another point to make about the use or therapeutic effects of herbs is that they are most effective when combined in formulas. It is rare to find herbs sold alone in Ayurvedic pharmacies. There are some exceptions, like Amla and Shatavari. Herbs are known to be much safer and stronger therapeutically when combined with other herbs that promote and harmonize their respective actions. Ayurveda also has many ways to potentize the herbs and formulas. This results in a much greater therapeutic effect than just taking an herb alone. For this reason Ayurvedic herbs are generally sold in formulas, or the doctor will have his compounder prepare a formula on the spot for a client. The best method of herbal treatment is to have your doctor prepare or give you a ready-made formula that will balance and harmonize your particular constitution. Herbs taken alone will have a less harmonious action on the body in general. I recommend that you study the books recommended earlier, for they will clarify the Eastern approach to herbs, various formulations, and the correct vehicles to take them with (i.e., water, honey, milk, etc.).

FAMOUS AYURVEDIC HERBS

AMLA,Amalaka (Emblica officinalis, Gaertn.)

Taste:Sweet,sour,and astringent
Attribute: Oily
Potency: Cold
Long-Term: Sweet

General" Action: Digestive stimulant, rejuvenating,
   antioxidant
Specific Action: Aphrodisiac
Therapeutic Action: Balances all three humors; very good
   for high pitta

Amla is perhaps the single most often mentioned herb in
the Caraka Samhita. It has a reputation as a powerful rejuvenating herb and is used in many Ayurvedic rejuvenation formulas, the most famous of which is Chavana
Prash. Amla is especially useful for pitta constitutions, as
it has a cold potency, but it will not aggravate the other
humors. The fruit is reputed to have the highest content of
vitamin C of any natural occurring substance in nature. It
promotes ojas and the reproductive fluids, and is useful in
the treatment of ulcers and hyperacidity.

   Modern scientific research has found many different
uses for the fruit, the part predominantly used in
Ayurveda. For example, a research team discovered that
when amla is taken regularly as a dietary supplement, it
counteracts the toxic effects of prolonged exposure to environmental heavy metals, such as lead, aluminum, and
nickel. These metals are prevalent in the environment of
industrialized countries. In the studies the pro-oxidant or
oxygen radical scavenger qualities of amla suggest that it
is also very effective in lowering the risk of many cancers.[5]
Other studies indicate that it is much more effective than
vitamin C alone in reducing chromosomal abnormalities.[6]
Amla juice has twenty times more vitamin C than orange
juice, and natural tannins prevent oxidation of the vitamin
content in a dry condition—in other words, it is heat stable. Studies indicate that the naturally occurring vitamin
C is easier for the body to absorb than synthetic vitamin
C. This and other studies indicate that naturally occurring
vitamin C may be ten times more beneficial to the body

---

[5]Dhir, et al, *Phytotherapy Research,* vol. 4 NE5 1990:175. See also "Modify-
infc role of Phyllanthus, " *Cancer Letters,* NE59, Elsevier Scientific Publishers
Ireland, Ltd. 1991:9-18.
   [6]A. K. Giri, *et al, Cytologia* 51, 1986:375-80.

than synthetic vitamins. The vitamin C content of amla is between 625 mg-1814 mg per 100 grams! [7]

Other studies[8] show that amla increases red blood cell count and hemoglobin percentages, and patients started their anabolic phase (metabolic processes involved in protein synthesis) sooner. The dried fruit reduced cholesterol levels, and no irritant or tumor-promoting activity was found, indicating that amla is safe to consume on a long-term basis.

Amla reduces unwanted fat because it increases total protein levels; this is due to its ability to create a positive nitrogen balance [9] and it also significantly reduces the levels of free fatty-acids.[10] In addition, amla, in a raw or natural form, reduces cholesterol[11] and reduces cholesterol induced atherosclerosis (obstruction of the arteries), making it a useful natural product to fight obesity. One study shows that it prevented atheroma (degeneration of the artery walls due to fat and scar tissue). Furthermore, amla has exhibited considerable effect in inhibiting the HIV virus which ultimately results in the disease AIDS.[12]

Therefore, one can draw the conclusion that amla is good for almost everyone on a regular basis. It reduces or eliminates the risk of environmental pollutants, normalizes cholesterol, reduces unwanted fat, cures ulcers, reduces or prevents cancer, has the highest content of vitamin C of any natural source, detoxifies the body, regulates digestion, has inhibiting effects against the HIV virus, promotes metabolic function and can produce these results

---

[7]The Wealth of India, vol. III (New Delhi, India: Council of Scientific & Industrial Research, 1952).

[8]"Records of Usage or Assays in Phyllanthus," Journal ofEthnopharmacology NE 30, Elsevier Scientific Publishers Ireland, Ltd., 1990:248-255.

[9]A. Tiwari, et al, Journal of Indian Medicine, 2 (1968),198.

[10]M. Tariq, et al, Indian Journal of Exploratory Biology, 15 1977:485.

[11]A. Jacob, et al, European Journal of Clinical Nutrition (EJC), 1988 Nov. 42(11):939—44.

[12]S. Mekkawy, et al, Chemical Pharmacy Bulletin, Tokyo, CZP, 1995 Apr. 43(4):641-8.

in a dried, natural, unprocessed form. The only thing that could possibly be better than amla for a daily herbal supplement is the Triphala formula, of which amla constitutes one third (see triphala).

Dose: 2 to 4 grams per day with meals

ASHWAGANDHA (Withania somnlfera, Dunal)

Taste: Bitter and astringent
Attribute: Light and oily
Potency: Hot
Long-Term: Sweet
General Action: Rejuvenating, tonic, corrects impotency increases ojas, corrects debility, reduces stress, immunomodulator, antitumor
Specific Action: Aphrodisiac, rejuvenating
Therapeutic Action: Lowers vata and kapha, okay for pitta in moderate doses unless toxins are present

Ashwagandha is one of the main herbs for promoting ojas and rejuvenating the body in Ayurveda. It is a well-known semen promoter and it treats impotency and infertility. It is used in many general tonics and preparations, such as Chavana Prash. Ashwagandha is especially good for lowering vata in men or women, and rejuvenating vata sites in the body, such as bone marrow (the site of B and T cell production). Although considered to be the primary tonic for men, it can be safely used by women for up to one year in cases of general debility, pregnancy, and high vata.

Clinical studies show that ashwagandha has antibacterial, antitumor, anti-inflammatory and immunomodulating properties.[13] A separate study also showed immunomodulatory (harmonizes immune function) effects including a positive effect on the central nervous system

[13] R. D. Budhiraja, et al, Indian Journal of Medical Research, 1987 46(11):488-91.

These tests show strong anti-stress actions, increased memory, and learning capabilities.[14] The strong anti-stress properties include both mental and physical stress and exhaustion. Furthermore, this test indicates the low order of toxicity of the plant, supporting the Ayurvedic view that it is safe for long-term consumption[15] It has also exhibited antibacterial and antifungal activities in a raw or unprocessed state[16] and it has antibiotic effects.[17] Many studies have documented the profound antitumor action of ashwagandha, suggesting possible anticancer effects.[18]

Other studies substantiate the tonic effect on the heart and lungs that Ayurveda has known about for so long. One study showed a prolonged hypotensive (stabilizes low blood pressure), bradycardiac (regulating heartbeat), and respiratory-stimulating action.[19] In tests on the central nervous system mild depressant effects were noted, but when electroshocks were administered, ashwagandha actually protected the subjects. This indicates the strong nourishing and protective effect it has on the nervous system.[20] Large doses of the root show radio-protection from X-rays.[21] In addition the anti-arthritic effects,[22] the prevention of necrosis of liver tissue, the rejuvenation of these liver tissues (which can reduce death

[14] S. Ghosal, et al, Phytotherapy Research, 1989 3(5):201-6.

[15] S,K. Bhattacharya, et al, phytotherapy Research, 1987 1 (1):32-7.

[16] S.. U. Kazmi, et al, Pakistan Journal of Pharmacological Science, 1991 4(2): 113-23.

[17] J. Mohan Das, et al, Indian Journal of Biochemistry, 1964 1(3): 157-8.

[18] H. Das, et al, Indian Journal of Cancer Chemotherapy, 1985 7(2):59-65 and S. K. Chakraborti, et al, Experienta, 1974 30(8):852-3.

[19] C. L. Malhotra, et al, Indian Journal of Medical Research, 1961 49:448-60; and Indian Journal of Physicological Pharmacology, 1960 4:49-64.

[20] S. Parsad, et al, Indian Journal of Physicological Pharmacology, 1968 12(4): 175-81.

[21] G. Ram, et al, Studying Biophysics, 1984 103(1):37-40.

[22] J. Sadique, et al, Acta Pharmacological Toxicology Suppl., 1986 59(7):406-9.

probability)[23] and the intestinal anti-inflammatory actions[24] of ashwagandha clearly show why Ayurveda has such a high opinion of this herb as a general tonic.

Dose: 2 to 4 grams per day with milk (or warm water)

BIBHITAKI (Terminalia belerica, Gaertn.)

Taste: Astringent
Attribute: Cold and oily
Potency: Hot
Long-Term: Sweet
General Action: Digestive stimulant, purgative, promotes eyesight and hair growth, anti-viral
Specific Action: Rejuvenating
Therapeutic Action: Reduces kapha and pitta; increases vata

Bibhitaki is used primarily to lower kapha-related diseases and respiratory disorders, such as coughs and bronchitis. Diseases are said to fear it because of its strong purgative action throughout the body. It can expel stones or other kapha-type accumulations in the digestive, urinary, and respiratory tracts. It is also a strong rejuvenator of the body, especially for the voice, vision, and hair.

Recent research shows that bibhitaki reduces levels of lipids (important dietary constituents that are insoluble in water; they contain vitamins and essential fatty-acids; in excess they cause fat buildup in the tissues) throughout the body and specifically lower the lipid levels in the liver and heart. This shows a strong action in preventing heart and liver fat congestion, which can lower the disease risk associated with those organs.[25] Other studies indicate that bibhitaki has retroviral actions in inhibiting the viral

[23]N. Singh, et al, Crude Drug Research, 1978 16(1):8-16.

[24]S. Somasundaram, et al, Biochemical Medicine, 1983 29(2):259-64.

[25]H. P. Shaila, et al, International Journal of Cardiology (GQW), 1995 Apr. 49(2):101-6.

growth in leukemia patients,[26] and yet another study indicates the strong inhibiting effect bibhitaki has on the HIV virus.[27]

As a daily rejuvenating and preventative supplement bibhitaki is superb, especially for kapha body types. Bibhitaki reduces excess body water, fat, and slowly regenerates the body on a tissue level. For people prone to viral infections, or a history of leukemia in the family, bibhitaki is a recommended daily supplement, alone or in the triphala formula.

Dose: 2 to 4 grams per day with meals

BRAHMI, Gota Kola (Hydrocytle asiatica, or
Centella asiatica, Linn.)

Taste: Bitter, sweet
Attribute: Light
Potency: Cold
Long-Term: Sweet
General Action: Rejuvenating, laxative properties,
    promotes intellect, voice and memory
Specific Action: Rejuvenates the brain
Therapeutic Action: Balances all three humors

Traditionally brahmi is used as a mental tonic, to rejuvenate the body, as a promoter of memory, as a nerve tonic, as a blood purifier, and for healing all kinds of skin diseases, including leprosy. It is one of the best satvic herbs known, and its use promotes a calm, clear mind, and improves mental function. It has a reputation for promoting long life and is used in many rejuvenating compounds.

Modern research seems to support many of the traditional claims of Ayurveda. A study of brahmi shows that it improves memory and helps overcome the negative effects

---

[26] O. Suthienkul, *Southeast Asian Journal of Tropical Medicine* (UVN), 1993 Deec. 24(4): 751-5

[27] S. Mekkawy, *et al*, *chemical pharmacy Bulletin*, Tokyo, CZP,1995 Apr. 43(4):641-8

of stress. The memory retention of learned behavior on test subjects treated with a water extract of brahmi increased three to sixty times as compared to the control subjects. This study also showed no level of toxicity up to a dose of 2.5 pounds per adult (at a body weight of 154 lbs).[28]

Brahmi is high in minerals, such as calcium, sodium, magnesium, potassium, phosphorous, aluminum, and iron. Brahmi is known as an antibacterial, antifungal, anti-amoebic, insecticidal, vulnerary substance. It has mild sedative effects; it is an anti-inflammatory externally; it is an adatogenic tonic, alterative, anti-rheumatic, restorative, nervine. It is a relaxant to the whole nervous system; it is cerebrovascular stimulating, a circulatory stimulant, and it accelerates wound healing.[29]

A popular compound made from brahmi, Brahmi Rasayan, an herbal jelly, was proved effective as a nerve tonic. Its effect included the whole nervous system, enabling the subjects to withstand a variety of tests.[30] There are many other modern studies that come to these same conclusions, conclusions that the ancient sages came to thousands of years ago. It is said that many yogis still use this plant in its fresh form as food and as an aid in meditation. The best Ayurvedic brain and memory formulas contain brahmi, as do many of the long life promoting compounds.

Dose: 500 mgs to 1 gram twice per day

GUDUCHl,Amrita (Tinispora cordifolia, Willd.)

Taste: Pungent, astringent, and bitter
Attribute: Light
Potency: Hot
Long-Term: Sweet
General Action: Immunostimulant, digestive aid
    rejuvenating, nourishing

---

[28]K. Nalini, *et al, Fitoterapie,* 1992, 63(3):232-37.
[29]D. Rohrs, *Australian Journal of Medical Herbalism,* 1990, vol. 2(2):27-8.
[30]Shukia. *et al, Journal of Ethnopharmacology,* 1987 21(1):65-74.

Specific Action: Rejuvenating
Therapeutic Action: Lowers pitta, balances all humors

Guduchi is considered to be a prime rejuvenating herb; its other name is Amrita, or nectar. Amrita is known in Hindu mythology to be an elixir that imparts immortality and health, in other words, it is a rejuvenating food. It is one of the best herbs for healing and rejuvenating in Ayurveda.

Modern research shows it to be a strong immunostimulant with very good anti-cytotoxic (drugs used in treating cancer) effects.[31] The use of guduchi helps to reduce effects of these toxic cancer-fighting drugs, and with its immune-promoting qualities, could even prevent cancer. Other studies show the ability to lower blood sugar in diabetic animals.[32] Another study shows it to be effective in reducing rheumatic complications.[33] Guduchi is an excellent herb to take as an immune booster and general tonic.

Dose: 1-2 grams twice per day

GUGGULU (Commiphora mukul, Hooker, Stedor)

Taste: Bitter, astringent, and sweet
Attribute: Subtle, slimy, and non-slimy
Potency: Hot
Long-Term: Pungent
General Action: Aphrodisiac, promotes overall strength
    digestive stimulant, regulates metabolism
    anticholestrol
Specific Action: Rejuvenating
Therapeutic Action: Lowers kapha and vata, does not
    aggravate pitta unless taken in high doses or for long
    periods

---

[31]U. M. Thatte, *et al, Methods Find. Experimental Clinical Pharmacology* (LZN), 1988 Oct. 10(10):639-44.
    [32]K. Raghuunathan, *"et al, Indian Journal of Medical Research,* 1969 3(2):203-09.
    [33]V. B. Mhaiskar, *et al, Rheumatism,* 1980 16(1):35-39.

Ayurveda has a high respect for Guggulu, which is a dark gum from a small tree. It is related to the myrrh tree and is the basis for many different compounds in Ayurvedic medicine. Guggulu is usually mixed with other herbs to enhance and guide them to a specific action in the body. It is considered to be a strong rejuvenating and purifying substance. Guggulu is reputed to have aphrodisiac properties, it reduces fat, toxins and other excess matter in the tissues. Effective in treating arthritis, digestive disorders, and many other problems, such as diabetes and ulcers.

Modern research shows that it is the prime Ayurvedic herb for treating obesity and high cholesterol. Recently a synopsis report was printed in a medical journal that highlighted the main qualities of this plant.[34] Studies over the last two decades clearly show that guggulu, in a crude unrefined form, lowers serum cholesterol and phospholipids, and that it also protects against cholesterol-induced atherosclerosis. Guggulu was seen to lower body weight in these clinical studies. Other studies show substantial reduction in all the serum lipids including cholesterol, triglycerides and phospholipids. Non-esterified fatty acids were also lowered. Guggulu was devoid of any adverse effects on liver function, blood sugar, blood urea, and other related items, proving its safety for daily use. In more than twenty years of clinical studies no reports exist of any side effects; this clearly shows guggulu as the prime substance in weight and cholesterol control.

Dose: Two 450mg tablets with meals, three times per day

HARITAKI (Terminalia chebula, Retz.)

Taste: Astringent, sweet, sour, pungent and bitter
Attribute: Oily and light
Potency: Hot
Long-Term: Sweet

[34] G. V. Satyavati, *Indian Journal of Medical Research,* 87 1988 April pp. 327-35.

General Action: Digestive stimulant, laxative, rejuvenating, aphrodisiac, antibacterial, antitumor antiviral, antioxidant
Specific Action: Rejuvenating
Therapeutic Action: Balances all three humors; very good for high vata

Haritaki is called the "king of medicines" in Tibet and is always listed first in the Ayurvedic materia medica because of its extraordinary powers of healing. In Ayurveda it is considered to destroy all diseases and eliminate all waste from the body. At the same time, it is known to promote tissue growth and health. Many Ayurvedic formulas have some amount of haritaki in them or are processed in it because of its high regard in Ayurvedic pharmacology.

Haritaki is used to treat digestive diseases, urinary diseases, diabetes, skin diseases, parasitic infections, heart diseases, irregular fevers, flatulence, constipation, ulcers, vomiting, colic pain and hemorrhoids. If taken after meals it prevents imbalance of any of the humors due to bad food or drink. It promotes wisdom, intellect and eyesight.

Modern science has found that haritaki has a strong effect against the herpes simplex virus (HSV),[35]has antibacterial activity[36] and exhibits strong cardiotonic properties.[37]Haritaki also has antioxidant components, which indicates it can increase the life of tissues.[38]Yet another study shows the anti-tumor activity of haritaki[39] and another study shows that it has considerable effect in inhibiting the HIV virus which ultimately results in AIDS.[40]

[35]M Kurokawa, et al, Antiviral Research Journal, 617, 1995 May 2(1-2): 19-37.M.

[36]A. Phadke, et al, Indian Journal of Medical Science (GJP) 1989 May 43(5): 113-7

[37]R. C. Reddy, et al, Fitoterapia, vol. LXI NE 6 (1990):517-25.

[38]J. S. Kim, et al, Han'guk Nonghwa Hakhoechi, Korea, 1993 36 (4):239-43.

[39]S. Lee, et al (KRICT), Arch. Pharmacological Research, Korea, 1995 18(2): 118-20..

[40]S. Mekkawy, et al, Chemical Pharmacy Bulletin, Tokyo, CZP, 1995 Apr. 43(4):641-8.

Thus, haritaki can be seen to be a valuable addition to anyone's herbal collection. With its rejuvenating and cleansing properties, haritaki is excellent for the digestive system. As a preventative supplement it has great anti-viral attributes, as shown by its antitumor and HIV action. It also is effective for alleviating constipation in general, and is helpful for vata persons because it works directly on the apana prana that lives in the colon. Taken in the triphala formula it is a well balanced digestive and rejuvenating aid.

Dose: 2 to 5 grams per day

KUMARI, Aloe (Aloes barbadensis,Mill.or Aloe vera, Linn.)

Taste: Bitter, astringent, pungent
Attribute: Slimy
Potency: Cooling
Long-Term: Sweet
General Action: Tonic, purgative, aphrodisiac,
    rejuvenating
Specific Action: Rejuvenating
Therapeutic Action: The fresh gel is balancing for all three humors; dry powder will aggravate vata and tends to constipate

Kumari means "young girl," implying the great rejuvenating properties of this plant. Kumari is good for numerous things, but excels in treating problems of pitta-related liver troubles, or as a female tonic. As a general female tonic it is best combined with shatavari for a more balanced effect. However, kumari is not recommended during pregnancy.[41]

Traditionally Ayurveda has used kumari for treatment of intestinal worms, liver and spleen imbalances, as a laxative, and as a tonic for the uterus. It is useful for any kind of pitta conditions, ulcers and inflammation, both in-

---

[41]Frawley and Lad, *Yoga of Herbs*, p. 100.

ternally and externally. It is considered an aphrodisiac and good for venereal diseases. Some modern studies have shown it effective in treating dyspepsia, flatulence, intestinal colic, general debility, cough, asthma, and as promoting hair growth.[42] Kumari is well known in the United States and its uses are numerous; however, it excels in treatments of the female reproductive system and conditions of the liver and spleen.

Dose: 2 tablespoons of gel twice per day or 1/2 cup in the morning

KATUK1, Kutki (Picrorrhiza kurroa, Royle & Benth)

Taste: Pungent
Attribute: Non-fatty, and light
Potency: Cold
Long-Term: Bitter
General Action: Liver tonic, blood purifier, antioxidant, anti-asthmatic, immunomodulator
Specific Action: Immunomodulator, liver tonic
Therapeutic Action: Lowers pitta and kapha

Katuki is used in Ayurveda for diseases of the liver and lungs. It has also been used to cure vomiting and fever. It is primarily known as an effective remedy against asthma. Several Ayurvedic formulas against asthma use katuki as the main herb. It is also known to have a tonic action on the body.

There have been an enormous amount of studies on katuki, and it is starting to appear in the United States as Picrorrhiza. The majority of these studies focus on either its liver-protecting properties or its proven anti-asthmatic qualities. Scientists have been able to isolate the active principal of katuki that combats liver dysfunction. Not only has katuki shown liver-protective abilities[43] it has

---

[42]V. V. Sivarajan, *Ayurvedic Drugs and their Plant Sources* (New Delhi India: Oxford Publishing, 1994) p. 261.

[43]R. A. Ansari, *et al, Indian Journal of Medical Research,* 1988 87(4):401-4.

Also shown a significant reversal of damage[44] These results have been proven in several different studies[45] and are now of great interest to pharmaceutical companies. In many studies the natural extract of katuki has proved more effective than the commonly used medicine for the liver.[46] Another study has shown it to reverse the hepatotoxic effects of drugs like paracetamol; this in turn has a beneficial action on the whole metabolism and reduces many of the secondary effects of modern drugs.[47]

Modern studies have also confirmed katuki's antiasthmatic properties. One study calls it the most effective compound in preventing allergen and PAF-induced bronchial obstructions. Reports show the effectiveness is more than 80 percent when compared to the controls.[48] There are many other studies that reach the same conclusion. Katuki works directly on inhibiting the release of histamine in the lungs; this then can prevent the asthmatic attack from happening.[49]

Perhaps even more interesting for most people is the antioxidant action of katuki. One recent study has proved that katuki is an antioxidant and a scavenger of oxygen free radicals.[50] This is really good news because recent evidence points to free radicals as being the primary cause of many diseases, such as cancer, heart attacks, HIV, and even arthritis. Well known antioxidants like vitamins C and E have shown excellent rejuvenating qualities due to their ability to fight off these free radicals. Another study shows that katuki has immunomodulating properties.[51] It

[44]Dwivedi, et, al, phytotherapy Research, 1991 5(3):115-19

[45]Kloss, et al, OOffen. (German) 27 Jan 1972 16pp.

[46]B. Shukla, et al, Phytotherapy Research, 1992 6 (1):53-5

[47]R. A. Ansari, et al, Journal of Ethnopharmacology, 1991 34(1):61-8

[48]W. Dorsch, International Arch. Allergy Immunology, 1992, 99(2-4):493-5.

[49]S. S Mahajani, et al, International Arch. Allergy Immunology, 1976, 53(2):137-44

[50]Chander, et al, Biochemical Pharmacology, 1992 44(1):180-3

[51]Pandey, et al, Indian Journal of Physiological Phyarmacology, 1989, 33(1):47-52.

also has valuable anti-inflammatory qualities[52] and tests confirm that it is safe to use and has no cancer-forming actions.[53]

Thus katuki is an excellent liver tonic, anti-asthmatic and immune system regulator. Due to its bitter nature it should not be ingested daily unless it is in a balanced formula. Otherwise it will have a depleting effect after several months.

Dose: 1 to 2 grams twice a day when needed

LICORICE,Mulethi Yastimadhu(Glycyrrhizaglabra; Linn.)

Taste: Sweet, bitter
Attribute: Heavy
Potency: Cold
Long-Term: Sweet
General Action:'Promotes strength, rejuvenating, building, lung tonic, and immunostimulant
Specific Action: Rejuvenating
Therapeutic Action: Can increase kapha, lowers pitta and vata

Licorice has long history as a rejuvenating herb in Ayurveda. It has a harmonizing action in the body and in herbal formulas. It is a very good lung tonic and known to be effective in fighting bronchitis. It is considered to be an immunostimulant and in Ayurveda it is known to promote peace of mind. Licorice has the ability to reduce infection and fight viral growth. It also promotes the growth of naturally occurring antibodies in the body. Strong anti-ulcer actions and an overall soothing effect on the digestive system have been documented. The majority of people can benefit from the regular use of licorice; the exceptions are high kapha and persons with hypertension. It is an excellent rejuvenating herb for pitta and vata persons.

---

[52]Engels, et al, FEBS Letters, 1992, 305(3):254-6.
[53]Jain, et al, Fitoterapia, 1992 63(3):255-7.

Dose: 1 to 2 grams twice a day, or take as an infusion freely

MANJISHTA, Indian Madder (Rubia cordifolia, Linn.)

Taste: Bitter, sweet, astringent
Attribute: Heavy
Potency: Cold
Long-Term: Pungent
General Action: Blood purifier, antitumor, antibacterial, aids circulation, is used to treat the female reproductive system, voice, skin, urinary system
Specific Action: Blood purifier
Therapeutic Action: Lowers pitta and kapha; increases vata

Manjishta is one of the best herbs for lowering pitta-type problems and balancing pitta people. It is useful for cooling the blood, stimulating the circulation, and promoting a healthy menses for women. Manjishta is good for all kinds of inflammations and can be used externally as a paste to heal the skin. As a blood purifier it has a strong action on the overall complexion, cleaning it of toxins and promoting a natural luster. Manjishta cools, detoxifies, and strengthens the liver, spleen, and kidneys. Recent studies show that it has antitumor properties[54] and yet another study showed antibacterial activity.[55] Manjishta is an excellent herb for women, and is used for pitta-type disorders of the blood.

Dose: 1 to 2 grams twice per day

NEEM, Nimba (Azadiracta indica,A.Juss.)

Taste: Bitter
Attribute: Light

---

[54] Tobishi Pharmaceutical Co., *Kokai Tokkyo Koho (Japanese)*, JP 59, 1984 April 28.
[55] Qiao, *et al, Yaoxue Xuebao,,* 1990 25(11):834-9

Potency:Cold
Long-Term: Pungent
General Action: Promoter of digestion, anti-inflammatory,
   heals skin, mouth, and teeth, antiparasitic
Specific Action: Antiseptic
Therapeutic Action: Lowers pitta and kapha, increases
   vata

Neem is an excellent antiseptic for the teeth and gums. It has been used for thousands of years as both a toothbrush (the twigs) and a stimulant for the gums. It has strong antiparasitic qualities and is an extraordinary blood purifier. As such, it also clears the digestive tract of parasites and toxins. Neem has a long history of outstanding results for all kinds of skin problems, even leprosy. Neem is included in most Ayurvedic skin products because it is as effective on an external application as through internal ingestion. It is also the best natural insecticide to use on crops or vegetables, as it prevents the insects from doing damage and yet remains non-toxic to humans.

   There is some concern in the Western scientific community about the safety of ingesting neem internally. In Ayurveda it has been safely used for over five thousand years internally and 70 percent of the population of India still uses neem twigs daily to clean their teeth, resulting in a very low rate of dental decay per capita. I personally used neem leaf pills for several years when I lived near Bombay. They were especially effective in the monsoon rains to prevent infections, colds, or fevers. Many yogis use neem for all their medical needs today as it has great versatility.

Dose: 500 mgs to 1 gram twice or three times per day

PIPPLI, Long Pepper (Piper longunm, Linn.)

Taste: Pungent
Attribute: Oily, light
Potency: Very hot
Long-Term: Sweet

General Action: Digestive stimulant, aphrodisiac,
   rejuvenating, purgative
Specific Action: Rejuvenating
Therapeutic Action: Lowers kapha and vata, increases
   pitta

Pippli is highly regarded in Ayurveda because of its long-term tonic effect on the body. While it is an excellent digestive stimulant, it is remarkable in that it has a sweet long-term action. As defined by the six tastes, sweet taste has a nutritive, building action. This makes it an ideal digestive stimulant for kapha and vata persons because vata can easily get depleted from digestive stimulants and kapha normally is increased by rejuvenating herbs, resulting in unwanted weight. Pippli is seldom taken alone, but is included in many Ayurvedic formulas as a stimulant and rejuvenator. The most famous formula with pippli is Trikutu, which combines pippli, black pepper, and ginger for a balanced digestive aid. Pippli is an excellent daily supplement for kapha persons.

Dose: 450 mgs to 1 gram with every meal

SHATAVARI (Asparagus racemosus, Willd.)

Taste: Sweet
Attribute: Heavy, oily
Potency: Cold
Long-Term: Sweet
General Action: Aphrodisiac, immunostimulant,
   anticancer, rejuvenating, promotes strength, promotes
   either semen or breast milk, and cures ulcers
Specific Action: Rejuvenating
Therapeutic Action: Promotes kapha, reduces vata and pitta

Shatavari is considered to be the best general tonic for women in Ayurveda. It has a slow, even action and can be safely used throughout a woman's life. Ayurveda uses shatavari for heat-related diseases as it has proved an effective remedy for peptic ulcers and hyperacidity for hundreds of years. It is also known to be a very good general tonic for both men and women, as it promotes growth and increases the humor of cohesion in the body—kapha. Tests show that it is an excellent aphrodisiac for men when mixed with ashwagandha; it promotes size, strength and stiffness of the penis.[56] It is included in numerous aphrodisiac formulas in the Caraka Samhita for both men and women.

Shatavari contains hormones called phytoestrogens that normalize estrogen levels in women. These hormones play an important role in preserving a woman's long-term health, preventing breast cancer, heart disease and osteoporosis. Recently studies indicate that naturally occurring phytoestrogens may prove safer for women because there is no increase in the risk of uterine cancer, as is possible with synthetic hormones.

Shatavari shows itself effective in killing the Candida bacteria and other digestive bacteria that can cause gas, bloating, and colic pain.[57] Another study shows that shatavari is excellent in treating general indigestion and naturally increases milk flow for lactating mothers.[58] It has also been shown to prevent abdominal adhesions that result after surgery[59] (showing its cohesive ability), and it has the capacity to reduce the effects of toxic cancer drugs (cytotoxic). These drugs, used to fight cancer, often leave a patient weak, sick, and toxic after treatment; shatavari is an immunostimulant and exhibits the ability to eliminate these toxins from the body and to relieve the effects caused by such drugs[60] Other studies show that shatavari has a strong anti-cancer inhibitory effect in breast cancer.[61]

---

[56]M. B. Reddy, et al, Indian Journal of Crude Drug Research, 1988 26(4): 189-96.

[57]N. N. Rege, et al, Journal of Postgraduate Medicine (JS7), 1993 Jan-Mar 39(1):22-5

[58]S. S. Dalvi, et al, Journal of Postgraduate Medicine (JS7), 1990 Apr. 36(2):91—4.

[59]N. N. Rege, et al, Journal of Postgraduate Medicine (JS7), 1989 Oct. 34(4):199-203

[60]U, M. Thatte, et al, Experimental Clinical Pharmacology (LZN), 1988 Oct. 10(10):639-44

[61] A. R. Rao, International Journal of Cancer, 1981, 28: 607-10.

As such, shatavari is an excellent daily supplement for all women (unless they are obese or have very high kapha; then consult a practitioner). It is also useful for men who have high pitta or hyperacidity. It is a strong tonic with documented immunostimulant properties.[62] The naturally occurring hormones are at a very low level, making it a safe hormonal supplement for all women throughout their lives. It is especially effective before, during, and after menopause. For nursing mothers and mothers recovering from childbirth, shatavari is close to a necessity to rejuvenate the mother's health and to promote a strong flow of milk for the child. Shatavari has all the elements necessary for a good women's general tonic and much more, too!

Dose: 2 to 6 grams per day with meals

SHILAJIT, Silajatu, Mineral Pitch (Asphaltum)

Taste: Pungent, bitter
Attribute: Light, oily
Potency: Hot
Long-Term: Pungent
General Action: Rejuvenating, urinary tonic, aphrodisiac, antidiabetic, antiparasitic
Specific Action: Rejuvenating
Therapeutic Action: Depending on the variety, it can be balancing to all the three dosas according to several Ayurvedic materia medica and the Caraka Samhita, but generally people say that it lowers kapha, vata, and increases pitta.

Shilajit is one of the prime Ayurvedic compounds for rejuvenating the body. It has a special effect on the kidneys, urinary system, and reproductive organs. It is included in many different formulas as it is said to enhance the effect of any herb with which it is combined. It is used in Ayurveda to treat diabetes and all debilitating urinary problems. It is used in consumptive type diseases, to treat asthma, the kidneys, hemorrhoids, anemia, epilepsy, skin diseases, and parasitic infections. It is also used to treat impotency and infertility, and as such it is considered to be an aphrodisiac

While Ayurveda considered shilajit to be of a mineral origin, the by-product of certain stones in the Himalayas, there is now strong evidence to show that shilajit is of vegetable origin. Shilajit is a black or brown bitumen-like tar that seeps out of certain rocks in the Himalayas during the hot summer. As early as 1942, tests concluded that neither bitumen nor mineral resins have any significant role in the formation of shilajit. Other studies in 1958, 1970, 1973, and 1976 have continued to uphold this finding and, in addition, have found a link to a cactus-like plant, Euphorbia royleana, Boiss. This plant is very rich in latex and has many of the same organic components, which indicate that the chemical constituents of shilajit are derived from the latex of the E. royleana plant. These findings have been supported by another study done in 1978 that actually discusses the manner of formation that results in the tar.[63]

The Caraka Samhita states that a person must use shilajit for a minimum of one month before starting to realize the regenerating effects. Shilajit is extracted from the rocks by boiling them, then it is stained off and cooked with Triphala. It is most often used in rejuvenating formulas, although it may be purchased in a tar-like form. This tar, or tablets, should be taken with milk twice to three times per day for several months.

Dose: 1 to 2 grams two or three times per day

---

[63]V. K. Lai, *et al, Ancient Science of Life, vol.* VII, NEs 3&4, Jan & April 1988 pp. 145-8.

SUNTHI, Sonth, Dry Ginger (Zingiber officinale, Rosc.)

Taste: Pungent
Attribute: Light, oily
Potency: Hot
Long-Term: Sweet
General Action: Digestive stimulant, rejuvenating,
  carminative, aphrodisiac, promotes voice
Specific Action: Aphrodisiac
Therapeutic Action: Lowers kapha and vata, increases
  pitta in excess

Sunthi is the dry variety of ginger and is slightly different in action than fresh ginger. The dry form is hotter and dryer than the fresh form, thus for reducing kapha and as a stimulant it is superior. The fresh form (ardraka) is better for colds, flu's, coughs, and for vata type problems. I grew up in Hawaii and as an adult I moved back to the Islands after eight years on the mainland. I discovered that fresh ginger was an excellent remedy for all cold symptoms and for sore throats. Whenever I have the beginnings of a sore throat I just cut a piece of fresh ginger and pop it into my mouth and suck on it until the irritation is gone from the throat. I do this as many times as needed until all symptoms have vanished. Pitta people may have to have food in their stomach in order to prevent aggravating the digestive bile.

  Ginger has a long history of medical use; it is perhaps one of the most used plants in the history of mankind. It is good for most diseases except in high pitta type problems such as inflammations, ulcers, etc. Ginger will normally not aggravate pitta in small doses or when used in cooking due to its sweet long-term action. This gives it a rejuvenating and nourishing effect on the body. It is well known to help respiratory diseases, arthritis, and the heart. Taken fresh before a meal with honey, it is considered to be excellent for kapha persons. It is included in many Ayurvedic formulas to act as a stimulant in the formula, which means it actually causes the formula to function better. The most famous formula that contains sunthi is the

Trikutu digestive formula. Contrary to some schools of thought, ginger is considered to be very effective in treating hemorrhoids when ingested regularly with food. Ginger infusions are a great beverage for kapha persons, and with a little licorice it makes an excellent drink for vata and pitta persons.

Dose: 250 mgs to 500 mgs with meals or as needed

FAMOUS AYURVEDIC FORMULAS

TRIPHALA FORMULA (amlataki, bibhitaki; haritaki)

Taste: Sweet, astringent, sour, pungent, bitter
Attribute: Oily
Potency: Cold
Long-Term: Sweet
General Action: Appetizer, rejuvenating, antioxidant
    cardiac tonic, mild laxative, and promotes eyesight
Specific Action: Digestive stimulant
Therapeutic Action: Triphala is an equal combination of
    amla, haritaki, and bibhitaki. It is a balanced formula
    for all the humors.

Tri = three; *phala* = fruits. Triphala is the best known
and most used formula in Ayurveda. It has been in
use for thousands of years. Triphala has all the properties of its three ingredients: amla, haritaki and bibhitaki.
The advantage of this formula is that it is milder in action and more balanced than any of the three alone.
When taken in large doses at night before bed, it has a
cleansing and detoxifying action; when 1/2 to 1 gram is
taken with meals, it has a building and rejuvenating
effect.

Used regularly it is good for gentle, slow detoxification of the digestive tract and then the deep tissues. It also
has the ability to normalize all three humors with continual use. As each of the three ingredients show strong inhibiting actions against the HIV and other viruses, this
formula should be considered as a daily dietary addition to
people working with, or exposed to, high-risk areas or people. The overall tonic effect of the these three fruits has
been known for thousands of years in India and other
Asian countries.

Prolonged use of triphala is safe and non-habit-form-
ing; in fact it rejuvenates the intestines, tissues, and cells
of the body, prevents cancer, and aids in weight loss. It is
known to promote the absorption of the B vitamins and to
improve the general absorption of all nutrients and vita-

mins contained in our food.[64] Triphala calms the apana prana and so helps in the absorption of prana in the colon. As a daily supplement triphala is hard to beat; that's why in India they say "even if your mother leaves you, everything will be fine if you have triphala."

Dose: 2 to 4 grams per day at bedtime, or 1 to 2 grams with meals

TRIPHALA GUGGULU FORMULA

The triphala guggulu formula is the best Ayurvedic formula to treat obesity and weight problems. Many studies have shown it to be effective in lowering cholesterol and reducing fat. This formula combines the best effects of both triphala and guggulu: the combined action is greater than the individual products. This formula has a balancing action on the whole metabolism, and its effects go way beyond weight loss. It is useful for any kind of metabolic problems, and it also has a strong effect on arthritis. This formula is effective in destroying toxins that accumulate in the tissues and fat in the body. Triphala guggulu should be used for at least three months as it works slowly, safely, and effectively on the metabolism.

Dose: 500 mgs to 1 gram at mealtime

TRIKUTU FORMULA (Tryusana)

Trikutu consists of long pepper (pippli), black pepper and ginger (sunthi) combined together in a more balanced way than each would be on its own. This is an excellent digestive formula for kapha and vata types, and for pitta persons with low agni (digestive fire). Trikutu promotes agni and increases pitta. It helps eliminate gas, bloating, colic pain, constipation, and other digestive complaints. It can

---

[64]Michael Tierra, *Planetary Herbology* (Twin Lakes, WI: Lotus Press, 1988), p. 132.

be used safely every day without any debilitating effects. Ayurveda uses trikutu in many formulas to aid in the assimilation of the other ingredients. Regular use increases the absorption of vitamins and nutrients

Dose: 450 mgs with meals

9
Diagnosis

❖ *I have Mentional only some of the diseases of the mind;*
although everyone is suffering from them.
only a few are able to detect them. ❖

Ayurvedic diagnosis is based on direct observation of the
body and personality of a person. Traditionally it is required that a student live and study with a teacher in
order to absorb this fine art. Diagnosis is definitely an art
in terms of the more subtle information that can be acquired. However, a great deal of information for self-care
can be gained quickly by a normal person.

Ayurvedic diagnosis is primarily concerned with the
management of the three humors. Thus all diagnostic
methods view either the harmony or disharmony of the
body in terms of excess or depletion of the three humors.
Therefore, each person is seen as an individual, not as an
average statistic. Each person's individual constitution is
basically unique, especially when combined with the mental constitution. This unique psychosomatic being is then
seen, according to Ayurveda, as an individual play of the
life forces. As the three humors are derived from prana,
one can look directly at the pranic balance of a person for
diagnosis.

Direct pranic diagnosis is very difficult. To observe the
pranic harmony of a person, either directly or indirectly,
requires extensive practice. The much easier method is
to observe the actions and manifestations of the three
humors. While they are still subtle, they are a step down
the ladder from observing the prana directly. With a little
practice, the more gross manifestations of the three
humors can be seen easily. It requires an adept of yogic

practices to directly see the balance of the pranas. My teacher is capable of this, and there are many interesting stories around his ability to spontaneously heal people. One account that I personally witnessed happened in the fall of 1991.

One morning about fifty people were sitting in the living room of my teacher's home. He lives in a house owned by his son and daughter-in-law. The house is quite small, so people were wall to wall, "sardine like," on the floor. One person was in a conversation with our teacher, Poonjaji. Just as the dialogue finished another man jumped up angrily and began to shout as he climbed over the other sardines. As he approached, Poonjaji just looked at him and waved a handkerchief that he was holding around the man, starting from a distance of fifteen feet and finishing at about two feet. When the man reached the two-foot point he was completely transformed. All anger had dissolved and he was peaceful and more than a little bewildered; he was no longer in emotional pain or anger.

As I was sitting to the right of Poonjaji, I was able to view what had actually transpired. He had made a joke out of the whole thing, as is his way, by acting like a matador, the man being a mad bull. So as he waved around the handkerchief he kept saying: "Toro! toro!" What I saw was very different. Poonjaji had instantly read the man's pranic balance, vasanas, and other mental habits in the subtle bodies. It is the prana that records and holds together all impressions and habits in the subtle bodies. As he was joking and waving the tissue, I watched in disbelief as he balanced and cleaned the psycho-somatic being coming toward him. As often happened with Poonjaji, what was coming out of his mouth was very different from what was in his face. He was intently working on this man while fifty people remained completely ignorant (almost!) of the pranic exchange taking place between him and the angry man. The result was an instantaneous healing.

I actually happen to know the man involved, and know him to be a gentle, kindly person, so I was a bit surprised at his actions, perhaps more than the results. On conversing with him the next day, he confirmed my observations. Later on the same day this event transpired, I had the chance to ask Poonjaji in private about the event. Actually I didn't ask, I bluntly told him what I had observed. With a twinkle in his eye, Poonjaji looked at me and changed the subject! This is only one of several events that I personally witnessed, and many, many more abound of the instantaneous diagnosis and treatment that have happened around him. This form of diagnosis and treatment is possible for a yogi. It may also happen around one who abides in the source—pure consciousness—but it happens without action or effort on the part of the one abiding in the source.

This kind of diagnosis and healing is not to be confused with energetic work common throughout the world. Methods like Reiki, hands-on healing, pranic healing and others work directly on the pranas, yet do not involve the instantaneous diagnosis or cure that results from an enlightened being or a yogi. These persons work on a much, much more subtle level of prana than the simple methods given above. Those methods that do teach some form of pranic diagnosis are superior to those that do not, because pranic diagnosis can be combined with Ayurvedic diagnosis for a very complete treatment, including changing the lifestyle, food, herbs, and mental disturbances. Since we are not yogis our diagnosis should be limited to the three humors and perceivable pranic congestion.

COLOR

In Ayurveda each of the three humors is associated with a color. Colors of wastes are somewhat different from external colors, like that for the complexion. Wastes have these color associations: vata with brown or black; pitta with yellow or green; and kapha with white. External or body parts are like this: vata is darkish, pitta is reddish, and kapha is pale or white. These colors are very helpful to distinguish which humor is in excess. These excesses can be seen on the tongue, in the stool and in the phlegm coughed up from the lungs or stomach. Externally they can be seen in complexion or on the skin in specific areas, such as the abdomen.

TONGUE

The easiest and best map of the body interior lies in the tongue. Tongue diagnosis can be very subtle, and the skill can be developed for many years. But, for the average person, it is relatively simple to understand immediately what is transpiring inside by looking at the tongue each morning. I teach most of my clients this method of self diagnosis to enable them to regulate their own health, especially toxic conditions of the digestion.

In Ayurveda, cleaning your tongue in the morning is like brushing your teeth, only more important. Normally one uses a metal tongue scraper to clean off the accumulation of gunk and to stimulate all the pranic nadis that terminate in the tongue. I was personally a bit skeptical about cleaning my tongue every day until I got a scraper (a thin U-shaped piece of metal) and did it. When I saw all the gunk—accurate description—coming off my tongue day after day I changed my opinion of the sages' habits of hygiene. Now I wouldn't leave home without my scraper!

The actual shape and color of the tongue can also show you your basic constitution. A thin trembling, pale tongue shows a vata constitution. A medium, reddish tongue is pitta, and a thick, roundish, pale and white tongue kapha. Normally, the tongue should be pink (see figure 7).

The first thing the tongue shows us is if any one humor is out of balance. Divide the tongue into three parts: the root is vata, the middle is pitta, and the tip is kapha (see figure 8). Excessive film (or gunk) in any of these areas shows which-humor is involved. Bumps, depressions, growths, or gunky build-ups all indicate which humoror humors are imbalanced.

When the tongue has a film over it, it indicates a build-up of undigested food or toxins in the body. The color of this film gives an indication of the humor that is

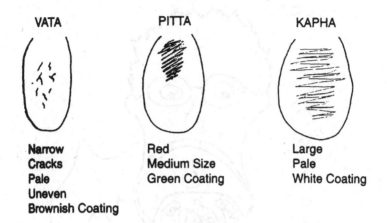

Figure 7. The three kinds of tongues

Figure 8. The three humors on the tongue.

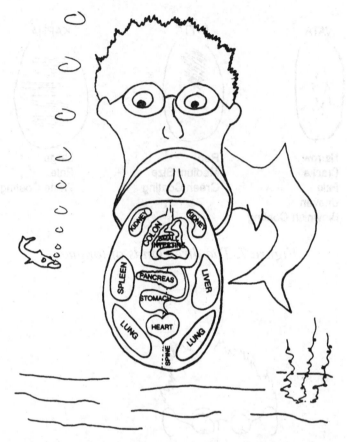

Figure 9. The organ locations on the tongue (mirror image).

causing the buildup. A darkish film is related to vata and a toxic, cold, dry condition. A yellowish or greenish film relates to pitta and a toxic, high heat condition. A whitish film is related to kapha, a condition of cold, oily, toxic congestion.

In addition, the exact location of the build-up gives an indication of which ofgan is affected or causing the problem. By looking at figure 9 (page 122), one can find the location where each major organ terminates as a meridian. The health of each region gives an indication of the corresponding organ's health. By the same token, bumps, depressions, etc., all indicate which organ is congested, over- or under-performing, or not healthy.

Determining what is actually wrong from what you view is, of course, real diagnosis. This requires study and experience, but here is what you can easily determine yourself.

Vata disturbances on the tongue
- Small cracks all over the tongue
- Dry, dark tongue
- Film over the back of the tongue
- Bumps on kidney points or colon area
- Film over large intestine and/or the small intestine
- Rough back area
- Small dark pimples

Pitta disturbances on the tongue
- Red tongue
- White cold sores
- Bumps on the liver, spleen, or pancreas points
- Greenish or yellowish film on the tongue
- Film on the middle section of the tongue
- Bright red patches over digestive organs

Kapha disturbances on the tongue
- White tongue
- Oily film on the tongue
- White coating or film on the tongue
- Depressions on the lung points
- Bump or depression on the heart point
- Tip of the tongue whitish or coated

Other general signs
- teeth indentation on the edge of the tongue indicates the malabsorption of nutrients
- deep line down the center of the tongue shows repressed emotions or nervous energy held on the spinal column

- cracks or kinks in the center line show back problems
- bad breath shows low agni (digestive ability) or toxic accumulation; check intestine points on the tongue for root problem

By compiling all this information one can quickly see the state of the digestive system. Often the general indications—such as many small cracks—equal a chronic vata imbalance, and are the most meaningful, as these give long-term indications of your overall past history. A cracked tongue, thick coatings, and strong colors (brown, red, white) all indicate an accumulation of humors over a period of time. Bumps or depressions also indicate chronic imbalances. In these instances, it is advised to visit an Ayurvedic practitioner, or if one is not available, a practitioner of Traditional Chinese Medicine. These professionals can help start you on a program to correct a long standing disorder.

THE PULSE

Pulse diagnosis is called Nadi diagnosis because through it the trained practitioner feels the pranic currents that control the humors and the organs. One hundred and four different pulse descriptions are given, although six are recognized as determining the individual's constitution.[1]

The wrist is the most common site for the pulse to be taken. The patient and practitioner should be calm and relaxed and clean for an accurate reading. Both should be seated comfortably. Drugs and alcohol affect the pulse; neither patient nor doctor should have used alcohol or drugs before diagnosis. The pulse changes according to the season and time of the day. Vata is best felt in the early morning, pitta is best felt in the middle of the day, and kapha is

---

[1]Dr. V. B. Athavale, *Pulse* (Bombay, India: Pediatric Clinics of India, 1976), pp. 22-24.

best felt in the mid-morning. These are the times of day that correspond to the given humor; this means that during these times that humor will be stronger and so, too, will the pulse.

Once on a visit to an Ayurvedic doctor that I respected in India (he was 84 at the time) I asked him to teach me pulse diagnosis. He doesn't speak much English and my Hindi is very basic, but we managed to communicate. The outcome was, after much amusement from his side, that I needed to take 10,000 pulses and come back. Well I didn't manage that week, and here I am a few years later, still practicing. In all likelihood he will be dead by the time I make the required 10,000. There was good reason from his side to ask for some preliminary work but, as it is not possible for me or most other Westerners to live with him for years in order to learn, Ayurveda is in danger of dying out.

This particular doctor is reputed to be one of the last five or six persons alive who knows how to purify mercury for human consumption in the traditional ways. This knowledge will die with him. He is an outstanding pharmaceutical doctor; this knowledge will die with him. This knowledge is traditionally passed from father to son, yet his son spent the whole time trying to sell me gems, rings, and trying to impress me with how much money he makes in America doing Ayurvedic consultations. This is really a very sad state of affairs. Although Ayurveda has seen an incredible upsurge in popularity in India and in the West, many of its secrets are dying with the older generation. Sadly, the commercialization of Ayurveda is partly responsible for the loss of many of its secrets.

Pulse diagnosis can be self-taught to an extent. I personally know of three different schools in regard to interpreting the pulse, and I believe that there are others. I personally use the system expounded by Dr. Vasant Lad.[2] To begin, simply take your own pulse three times a day for a few months. If you take the pulse according to the peak

---

[2]Dr. Vasant Lad, *Ayurveda: The Sciences of Self-Healing* (Twin Lakes, WI: Lotus Press, 1984).

times of the three humors you will see a big difference between each one. This will give you an incredible amount of information if you pay close attention and do it regularly. The best times are before breakfast, lunch and dinner.

Your pulse should never be taken after massage, after eating a meal, after drinking alcohol, after sunbathing, after sitting next to the heater or fireplace, after hard physical exercise, after sex, when hungry, while taking a bath. All of these activities increase one or two of the humors, which will then give you an incorrect diagnosis.

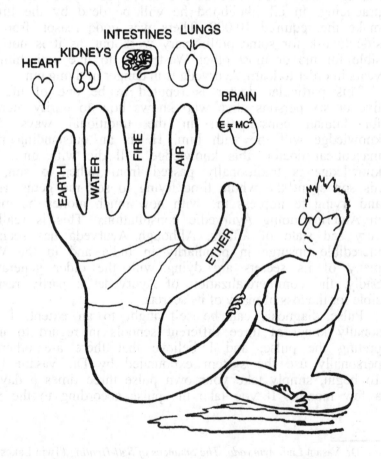

Figure 10. The five elements correspond to the five fingers.

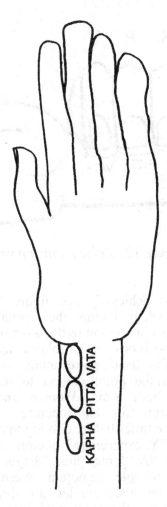

Figure 11. The three humors on the left wrist.

The five elements correspond to the five fingers (see figure 10). The three humors correspond to three positions on the wrist (see figure 11). By using the correct finger for the correct pulse position, more accurate information is obtained. The pranic currents are in harmony if the correct finger is used. In other words, if you use the air element finger on the vata point (which is composed of air) a more

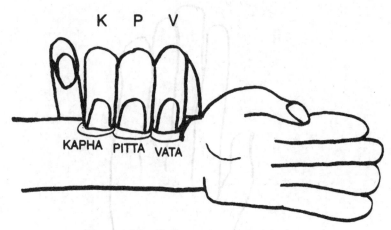

Figure 12. Pulse points on wrist.

accurate reading is achieved. See figure 12 for the correct finger placement when taking the radial pulse. Note the location of the fingers in relation to the wrist bone.

Of the three positions each relates to one humor. The point closest to the hand corresponds to vata, the middle point to pitta, and the point closest to the shoulder, kapha. This is true for both arms. Women and men should be tested on both arms for an accurate reading. The pulse should be taken three times before coming to a conclusion.

have seen VERY experienced doctors in India make constitutional mistakes by doing pulse diagnosis too fast in an effort to impress people (ignorant Westerners). The pressure should first be equal under all three fingers, slowly release the pressure, then unequal pressure by position, one, two, and three. The pulse should then be rolled under the three fingers. Repeat this three times.

These are only the basic guidelines and do not account for mixed constitutions. Nevertheless, these descriptions should still put you on the road to learning. Check your pulse several times at different times during the day to determine your primary humor. One time is not enough. Next take into account the two different levels, There are two distinct levels for each position—superficial and deep.

Figure 13. Vata pulse.

Figure 14. Pitta pulse.

Figure 15. Kapha pulse.

As there are three positions on each wrist, it means that you have six pulse readings for each arm—three superficial and three deep. This totals twelve positions. Start with the superficial level or shallow touch. This means lightly touching the skin. Next, apply harder pressure to take the deep pulse. Vata is usually found on the shallow level and kapha is usually found on the deep level. Pitta can be in both or between both.

The constitution is determined by several different impressions received by all three fingers when light, EQUAL pressure is applied, then firm, deep EQUAL pressure is applied.

- **Vata pulse** is felt as very rapid, shallow and irregular in any of the three positions (see figure 13, page 129).
- **Pitta pulse** is felt as a strong, regular beat in any of the three positions (see figure 14, page 129).
- **Kapha pulse** is felt as slow, deep, and weak in any of the three positions (see figure 15, page 129).

- You are mostly **vata** if your pulse is fast and irregular—80 or more beats per minute.
- You are mostly **pitta** if your pulse is strong and regular—70-80 beats per minute.
- You are mostly **kapha** if your pulse is slow and deep—below 70 beats per minute.

- If you feel a **vata pulse** (fast, irregular) in any other place than the first position (the vata position), then vata.is imbalanced.
- If you feel a **pitta pulse** (strong, regular) in any other place than the middle position, then you have an imbalance of pitta.
- If you feel a **kapha pulse** (slow, deep) in any other place than the last position (kapha position), then you have an imbalance of kapha.

- You have an overactivation of **vata** if the pulse is overly fast in the vata point.
- You have an overactivation of **pitta** if the pulse is overly strong in the pitta point.
- You have an overactivation of **kapha** if the pulse is overly strong in the kapha point.

- You have a deficiency of **vata** if you have a vata constitution and do not feel a normal pulse (i.e., over 80) in the vata point.
- You have a deficiency of **pitta** if you have a pitta constitution and do not feel a normal pulse (i.e., between 70-80) in the pitta point.

- You have a deficiency of **kapha** if you have a kapha constitution and do not feel a normal pulse (i.e., below 70) in the kapha point.

If you find a pulse in another position, i.e., vata in the middle (pitta) position, or pitta in the first (vata) position, it means that the humor has moved out of its home. This is an imbalance in the middle of the disease process. IT IS TIME TO DO SOMETHING NOW! At this point you may already be feeling some discomfort or you may be ignoring your body's signals. If you wait, your little problem will get bigger very soon. The humors are much more difficult to manage once they "leave home" (unlike when your children leave home—this is not a good sign!).

If you find your pulse in the correct position, but over-stated, i.e., vata very fast, pitta very strong, and kapha very weak, then you probably have an imbalance of your humor. It is easier to treat at this point because it has not "left home." This is the simplest situation because the humor is just treated by its opposite humor (see chapter 14). If left untreated, then the humor will move further out of its home and start to invade another humor, thus aggravating it also. In the "left home" scenario, two or all three of the humors can be disturbed. In the "aggravated at home scenario" (before the kids leave) only one humor is disturbed—only the one pulse that is overstated.

This represents the beginning of pulse diagnosis. As stated earlier, there are 104 different variations of the pulse acknowledged in Ayurveda. In order to master this method it is necessary to study with a teacher and develop intuition. However, if the above information is practiced and applied, then self-diagnosis is not only possible, it then becomes preventive health care.

Another aspect of pulse diagnosis is determining the overall harmony of the person. This is done by finding the natal constitution (prakriti) and comparing it to the constitution of the moment (vakurti). By comparing these two, one finds either balance or imbalance. If the two are the same, there is balance. If the two are different, there is imbalance. Thus, Ayurveda always perceives a person's harmony according to his or her birth nature versus his or her nature at the present moment. This is not a comparison to any book, idea, concept, statistic or rule. It is comparing you with you—a truly individual approach.

OTHER METHODS

Observation of the other parts of the body are of great value. The face, complexion, eyes, hair, and nails all give important information about the constitution and general health of a person. These methods are described very well in Dr. Lad's book and are worth studying. Dr. Frank Ros also gives excellent information on diagnosis and the pranic relation to every organ in the body; his book is highly recommended for further study.[3]

I personally learn a great amount from talking with people. This is called interrogation or questioning in Ayurveda. Aside from the obvious information that can be gained from talking to a person, such as, "It hurts here," or "I have constipation," the mental constitution is revealed. Ayurveda considers the mental constitution to be stronger than the physical constitution. This is especially important in relation to treating a person.

If a person is of the vata mentality, then one would not recommend any complicated treatment, and would give as few doses as possible during the day because vata is irregular. Tablets or capsules taken around meals would be easier for this vata type. If a person is of the kapha mentality, then regular visits are needed to keep his or her energy up and going. The pitta mentality person may be given powders and teas as he or she is often very determined when the importance of an issue is understood.

In this way the person's mental constitution can aid or nullify a treatment program. The mental constitution

---

[3]Dr. Frank Ros, *The Lost Secrets of Ayurvedic Acupuncture* (Twin Lakes, WI: Lotus Press, 1994).

will also decide eating habits, living habits, and other important factors involved in the healing program. If a person is very disturbed, then therapies that promote peace and harmony can be given. Certain herbs also help to promote a peaceful mind, such as bramhi and ashwagandha. The mental constitution is of great importance and must also be determined for an effective cure or effective management. See chapter 3 on constitution to remember all the different qualities of each mental humor. Please note that mental habits help determine the pranic habits that directly control the health of your body.

10
Weight Loss and Beauty Care

❖ *Vain is any enjoyment to a diseased body;*
vain are prayer and penance without devotion to Hari (God).
A handsome body is of no use without a soul and
all I have is worthless apart from Rama. ❖

True beauty is an inner phenomenon. How we feel about ourselves is the primary cause of beauty. The mental attitude that we have about ourselves shapes our individual expression of beauty. Real beauty reflects our own inner connection to the substratum of all creation, our true nature, Consciousness.

Each person has a natural beauty that results from this connection. When developed, this inner connection, which is the result of knowing your real nature, shines forth naturally to all beings. This kind of beauty is not dependent on the health of the physical body or its shape. It is a secondary effect of inner peace and contentment. This kind of beauty makes one loved by all. Physical beauty is completely relative to the social trends which may have nothing to do with beauty or the natural shape of men and women. Anyway, these trends are always changing with time and fashion; the social assessment of beauty today has little to do with real beauty.

Physical beauty starts with your spirit, then your mental attitude, your digestive ability, your food, and lastly your daily regime. All of these factors affect or are affected by prana. The more attuned you are to your source, the more prana or vitality you have readily available for use. Progressively, each item listed above either enhances or inhibits the amount of prana available to be utilized by the body. The basis of good health, including your external beauty, is your ability to access prana and to utilize it.

Prana is your vitality in the most physical sense. An inability to absorb prana leaves you with low vitality and a tired look. Without a good supply of prana it is difficult to feel and look healthy. Without this prana it is difficult to make the changes necessary to look and feel more beautiful. Insufficient or uncontrolled prana leads to self-destructive habits that prevent your natural beauty from showing. In relation to this, the classical eight limbs, or ways, of yoga are valuable to generate enough prana to change bad habits. The most important habits are right thinking, not harming others, right action, right living. "Right" in this sense means "that which promotes peace."

When you start to cultivate a lifestyle in harmony with peace the prana becomes peaceful. When the pranas in the body are agitated it is very hard to move toward changing old habits that may reduce your natural beauty. Aggravated prana disturbs the mind and all the nadis. Once the nadis become disturbed, the nervous system becomes affected and physical blocks result. Blocks in the nadis, due to agitated prana, cause dysfunctions in the metabolism. Diseases of a minor and major nature result from a disturbed metabolism.

Therefore, living as peacefully as possible, even if there is stress at home or at work, leads you to harmonize the pranas in the body. Peaceful living in turn generates more energy to change the bad habits that may cause a disagreeable external veneer over your natural beauty. Peaceful living is a choice that each person is capable of implementing. This is the first and most important step in revealing your natural beauty.

After peaceful living, speech becomes important. As stated earlier, we are often more concerned by what we put into our mouth than by what comes out of it. This is also one of the eight limbs of yoga—right speech. Being attentive to speak in a positive light, or not at all, increases access to prana, hence more vitality. Speaking badly or bitching diffuses your prana. Surely, we all have experienced meeting a nice looking person, perhaps even beautiful, who then starts bitching and saying nasty things. This way of speaking turns beauty into ugliness. Haven't we all had this experience? Isn't it clear how important to our beauty beautiful speech is? If this is not appropriate for the situation, leaving or remaining silent will maintain a high quality of undisturbed prana.

The next factor affecting beauty is our ability to digest the food we eat. This has been discussed in other chapters, but it is worth mentioning again because it is really an important factor as far as physical looks are concerned. The digestive ability is the ability to transform our food into energy and the means by which we eliminate toxins from the body, thus preventing their accumulation. Once the digestive fire falls low the toxins—in the form of undigested food—accumulate and pollute the body. Our skin quality, hair, and vitality all suffer from this pollution of the digestive tract. Toxins age our body much faster. Therefore, by not allowing them to collect, we live longer.

Detoxification methods should be undertaken along with therapies that increase the digestive fire. These are basic steps to increase, maintain, or recover our natural beauty. To clean the body out occasionally is just common sense. If you have any doubt in this regard just open up the drain in your kitchen sink. See what happens to the food that slowly builds up in the drain. If you are, say 30, look for a thirty-year-old sink drain and open it up. Remember, this is the same food and drink that you put through your digestive system. Periodic cleansing of the intestines increases your life span and enhances your beauty.

It is a well known fact in many cultures throughout the world that eating light meals twice a day increases the life span considerably. This causes less wear and tear on the intestinal tract. By eating less we are much less likely to accumulate the same amount of toxins that occur when large meals are taken too soon after the previous one, thus, not giving a sufficient amount of time for the full digestive process to take place.

Fasting can be useful to clean the body. However, I find that most Westerners are not comfortable with this method. Either they are uninterested or they overdo it. Fasting is useful, but care should be taken to determine your constitution before considering a fast. Vata people are the least suited for fasting. They should generally not fast or should do so only under the guidance of an Ayurvedic practitioner. Pitta people can fast for short periods, one or two days. Kapha persons can fast for longer periods of time, three to four days. Fasting is best done for one day one to four times per month. This is preferable rather than drastic cleansing fasts which drain the body's vitality—prana and stored nutrients—and generally shock the metabolism. If this kind of cleansing fast is appealing to you then it is best to consult an Ayurvedic practitioner to get advice on how to minimize the shock that occurs to the body. Ayurveda has been using fasting therapies for thousands of years and the results are well-documented for each constitution. If someone is advising you to fast without considering your constitution, then you are most likely damaging your body.

Care should also be taken by heavy or overweight people in regard to fasting. There is an interesting psychophysiological mechanism that comes into play during fasting. When a person deprives the body of food, it reacts by triggering survival instincts, which basically manifest as more hunger. The body is then getting conflicting signals from the brain and from the survival mechanism. When fasting is done for a day, this conflict is negligible. However, after two or three days the conflict will often cancel out any benefits that may have been gained. This is because the body thinks it is being starved—which it is—and so when food is consumed again, the body will try to take double the needed quantity of food in order to recover what it feels it "lost." This results in a no-win situation; it, in fact, aggravates the problem. These types of occurrences can be avoided by consulting and working closely with a qualified Ayurvedic practitioner.

WEIGHT LOSS

Ayurveda has long experience in weight loss programs. It is often forgotten that India was probably the richest country in the world for the longest time in recorded history. India was invaded by almost all neighboring cultures, ancient and modern, because of the natural wealth that abounded there. Just look at the world's richest woman, the Queen of England. Many of India's priceless gems and treasures are the basis of her wealth. Consequently, the diseases that are associated with an affluent culture, such as obesity, are well known in the Ayurvedic medical thesis. Recent studies performed in India give clear examples of this knowledge. A randomized double-blind, placebo-controlled clinical trial was performed by doctors from two different medical schools and the obesity clinic in the Nanal Hospital, Pune, India.[1]

In this study, seventy subjects were randomly divided into four groups. Three of the groups received Ayurvedic compounds and one group received a placebo. All subjects were at least 20 percent over their normal body weight and had no endocrinal disorders or diabetes. All subjects were in good health other than being obese. DIETARY INTAKE WAS NOT CONTROLLED. The treatment and study lasted for three months. Patients were examined every two weeks, during which time both subjective finds and actual body measurements were noted.

On completion of the study a significant weight loss was noted in all the groups treated by Ayurvedic compounds as opposed to the placebo group. There was a remarkable reduction in serum cholesterol and triglyceride levels in patients that received compounds. The common drug used was Triphala Guggulu (see chapter 8). Triphala is a combination of three fruits and Guggulu is the gum of a tree related to the myrrh family.

Triphala has strong purifying and antioxidant qualities as well as reducing the overall water content in the body tissues. Guggulu is known in Ayurveda to balance the whole metabolism and to increase the heat associated with tejas or the metabolic fire that digests the food. Guggulu

---

[1]Prakash Paranjpe, et al, *Journal of Ethopharmacology,* 29 (1990):1-11.

has a harmonizing effect on the body for it works through the metabolism.

Just think what kind of results could be achieved with a treatment of combined therapies. In Ayurveda such a combined treatment would entail detoxification, herbs to increase the digestive fire, a satvic vegetarian diet according to your constitution, daily exercise according to your constitution, massage, and triphala guggulu.

These methods are available to everyone today without undue cost or special equipment. High doses of determination, prana and self-love are recommended in conjunction with triphala guggulu. This compound is becoming more easily available in this country, as are other Ayurvedic herbs and formulas. Many Ayurvedic herbs are available by mail order if they are not available in your local heath food store. Look at chapter 14 to see how to increase the digestive fire or tejas.

Remember, Ayurveda does not support drastic methods that shock your body and metabolism. The best way is to slowly work toward an achievable goal. When this is achieved, another one can be set; in this way one gradually achieves the desired result. As obesity or overweight problems tend to plague kapha types, this slow but sure, method matches the kapha mental constitution.

There are several simple steps that anyone can do to lose weight. The following steps, if done daily, will help you to feel better in one week, and will help you lose several pounds each month. This will give you more energy and confidence to proceed further with other Ayurvedic therapies. Begin by doing the following:

- Sit down when you eat; never eat while walking or standing as it takes away energy (prana) from your digestive system.
- Do not read or watch TV while eating; this also takes energy (prana) from your digestion.
- Eat only when your stomach is empty, usually four hours after you have eaten the previous meal. This allows the previous meal to be fully digested.

- Do not take the next bite of food until the previous one is swallowed.
- Wait five minutes before taking another serving of food; usually you will not be hungry after waiting a few minutes.
- Eat whole fresh foods with abundant prana.
- Eat less.
- Enjoy what you eat! Eating is a pleasurable action; prepare your food with love and enjoy eating it.

The most important thing to cultivate is self-love. Inner well-being will result in weight loss, but weight loss will not necessarily result in self-love.

BEAUTY CARE

As stated above, external beauty depends on the general heath and the cleanliness of your body. Ayurveda has a very specific view of the interrelationship between each level of your body. In Ayurveda each level of the body nourishes the next level. If the preceding level is not in the best of health, then the following level will also be affected to some degree. The degree that it is affected depends on how long and how polluted the preceding level is.

These levels are called *dhatus,* or tissue levels. For a Westerner it is simpler to just perceive them as layers of the body, each giving nourishment and life to the next. In each level the basic ingredients consumed by the body— food and drink—become more and more refined. They also become more atomic or potent. The ultimate potency in the human body is the ability to create life. Thus the reproductive fluids are considered to be the highest, most refined, product of the body. The seven main levels are included with their sub-levels as follows:

1) Plasma and lymph fluids
        Mammary glands and fluids
        Menstrual flow

2) Red blood cells
   Blood vessels
   Muscle tendons
3) Muscles
   Skin
4) Fat and connective tissues
   Fatty tissue under skin
5) Bones
   Teeth
6) Marrow and nerves
   Hair on the head
7) Reproductive fluids
   Ojas

Not only does each level nourish the next level and its sub-levels, it also has a specific waste product. The secondary levels and waste products are important for beauty because they manifest as hair, nails, and body odor. It is difficult to feel beautiful or handsome if your breath smells like a dragon. Wastes from the body are listed below:

1) Mucous
2) Digestive bile
3) Ear wax, sinus mucous
4) Sweat
5) Nails, body hair
6) Tears
7) None

A healthy body level produces a healthy "waste." With this information you can look at the parts of your body that are not as healthy or radiant as you would like. For example, if I have a strong body odor—ode de dragon—I would look at the first four levels of the body. Even though sweat is the result of the fourth level, the other three are involved in its overall health. Just applying deodorant—ode de knight—will actually increase the problem while masking it. Deodorants seal the skin, which prevents the natural breathing needed to maintain health. If there is a strong odor, it is due to toxins in the level of the fatty tissues.

Bad breath comes from improper digestion and excessive bile production—level two. The health of your hair is related to the bone marrow and nervous system. If these two are in good condition, then strong healthy hair results. This information must be applied according to your individual constitution. Vata people will more often have dry and brittle hair because those are traits of the vata humor. Use the information relative to your body, and don't try to become another constitution.

Comparison to others is self-destructive. We are taught to compare ourselves with others from birth, and brainwashed to believe it is a factor in beauty, society and self-worth. Nothing could be further from the truth. The whole science of Ayurveda is based on recognizing people as individuals and developing therapies according to that understanding. Comparing places limits on your natural beauty and destroys self-love. Natural beauty shines for no reason.

Ayurvedic beauty care revolves around your constitution. You can also use treatments locally for problems even if that humor is not imbalanced. For example, if you have dry skin and have a predominately pitta constitution—this happens to me all the time—it can indicate an imbalance of vata or not. If the vata humor is not imbalanced then you may treat your skin with anti-vata treatment even though vata is not your natal constitution. If, as in the above example, the vata humor is involved, then treatment would first consider balancing the vata humor and then treating the skin. With Ayurvedic therapies you have many possibilities to balance and promote health. For further information on how to apply these therapies to beauty I highly recommend Melanie Sachs' *Ayurvedic Beauty Care*.[2]

Cleanliness is very important for beauty, yet Ayurveda recommends that little or no soap be applied to the skin. Soaps rob the skin of the natural oils that protect

---

[2]Melanie Sachs, *Ayurvedic Beauty Care* (Twin Lakes, WI: Lotus Press, 1994).

and nourish the skin. There are a number of natural products that clean the skin without removing the important protective oils that keep skin soft and young. Examples are the soap-nut and shitaki "soaps" and shampoos. These products—especially in powdered form— contain no harmful chemicals that clog or harm the skin. At an Ayurvedic pharmacy that produces beauty produce le owner told me that any liquid shampoo has chemicals in it—even if it says it doesn't—as they are needed to bind the fluid together.

Antioxidants play an important role in keeping the skin wrinkle-free and soft. Amla is a very good antioxidant and is used in many rejuvenation and beauty compounds. Daily use of herbs like amla, both internally and externally in oils, will increase your body's ability to stay young. Antioxidants, like vitamins C, A, and E, or amla, all slow the aging process by preventing oxidation of the body (*oxidation* literally means "the putrefaction of the tissues").

Massage plays a very important role in beauty care and the general health of the skin. The skin is an organ of elimination. Many toxins leave the body through the skin. Regular massage helps this detoxification of the body and keeps the skin young and soft. Ayurveda uses oils for massage rather than creams or other substances. Oil is food. Ayurveda states that you should not put something on your skin that you would not eat. Oils are usually mixed with herbs to help your particular constitution. Shatavari is often mixed with sesame seed oil for arthritis pain or just muscle fatigue.

Daily exercise in the form of yoga, Tai Chi, dance, or walking is very important for health and beauty. Exercise stimulates the metabolism and helps the body expel the toxins that pollute us and cause aging. Exercise also stimulates prana, circulating it throughout the body and allowing it to be absorbed more through breathing and movement. Without daily pranic stimulation it is difficult to remain healthy; prana is the basic building block of health and beauty.

Relaxation is as important for beauty as exercise. Without deep relaxation, prana remains active and disrupts the three humors through excessive activity. It also aggravates the nervous system. Relaxation promotes a peaceful quality of prana, which, in turn, soothes the nervous system. Action must be accompanied by inaction or an imbalance will result. Meditation is a very good form of relaxation because it works on a deeper level of the being than just the nervous system. Meditation connects us to our true source of beauty, our true nature, consciousness. Thus it is the most powerful tool to enhance beauty.

11

Pranic Healing on the Three Humors

❖ *No one in this world is so highly blessed as you, for you have*
sought the gift of devotion, which is the fountain of every blessing
and which even sages cannot win for all their infinite labors,
though they consume their bodies in the fires of prayer and yoga. ❖

It is possible to have a therapeutic effect on the three humors by using pranic healing. This method works directly
on the five pranas. Each prana corresponds to one of the
three humors and all correspond to the chief prana. Vata is
the humor most closely related to prana, as it is unseen,
unstable, and provides the principle of movement to the
other two humors.

I have used this method as a support to other more
common Ayurvedic therapies for several years. Pranic
healing was my first interest in the healing arts, and I
continue to use it daily. It is an excellent support to all
other Ayurvedic therapies because it works directly on the
prana, and therefore, the humors.

Pranic healing, while very effective, is best seen as a
supplemental aid to balancing vata. Because vata is unstable, the effects of pranic therapy are often lost in two to
three days. It is very difficult to make a lasting change in
chronic imbalances of vata with pranic healing. However,
pranic therapies can greatly increase the speed it normally
takes to control chronic vata imbalances. It should be said
that whatever you do for yourself is far stronger than any
outside aids. Pranic healing provides an excellent support
for vata management and is very effective in treating immediate disturbances in vata. As vata is the primary cause
of disease, the assistance of pranic healing should be wel-
comed by Ayurvedic practitioners.

Vata is traditionally treated directly with special enemas and colonics. Pranic healing offers a substitute to this
more traditional vata management. Often in today's world
it is neither practical nor possible to see a qualified
Ayurvedic practitioner to receive these kinds of therapies.
Pranic healing offers an option to direct vata management.
It is a method that one may learn and master within a
year depending on past experience and the amount of
practice done. It is also suitable for the very young and
old, those very sick or debilitated. As such, it can aid in the
actual application of Ayurvedic management methods in
the daily life.

Pranic healing as a method is explained clearly in
Prana: The Secret of Yogic Healing.[1] Therefore, this chapter will not explain the method, rather it explains the
therapeutic effects of the pranas on the three humors that
I have observed over the last several years of combining
more classical Ayurvedic therapies with pranic healing.

Having established that prana controls or is a refined
state of the vata humor it should be clear to all that any
direct change in the pranic currents will affect vata. The
knowledge that vata is the humor most responsible for disease, and most responsible for imbalances in the other two
humors has also been established.

Pranic healing is best used to control vata, but it may
also be used to harmonize the functions of both pitta and
kapha. Using pulse diagnosis I have clearly seen the direct
effects on vata before and after a pranic treatment. The results are less dramatic on the other two humors, but are
still easily felt with pulse diagnosis. Given below are the
effects by humor and how to best correct common diseases
associated with each humor. This is much easier than
treating diseases manifesting as one humor but caused by
another humor. My experience shows that harmonizing
the vata makes treating the more complicated forms of humoral imbalance somewhat easier.

---

[1]Atreya, Prana: *The Secret of Yogic Healing* (York Beach, ME: Samuel
Weiser, 1996).

To review, the functions of the five pranas (see figure 1, page 17) are as follows:

- Prana—the inward-moving prana; seated in the head and heart; controls thinking and emotions.
- Apana—the downward-moving prana; seated in the colon; controls all the processes of elimination.
- Samana—the equalizing prana; seated in the navel; controls the digestion and harmonizes the above pranas.
- Udana—the upward-moving prana; located in the throat; controls speech and expression.
- Vyana—the pervading prana; seated in the heart; unites the other pranas and the body, controls nerve and muscle action.

It should be noted that the prana resides primarily in the first subtle body after the physical body. This body completely permeates the physical body and therefore supplies prana (nourishment) to both the physical and subtle bodies. While the vata humor is seated in the colon, it is controlled directly by the Apana Prana, which controls the downward movement in the body. Thus, by working on the first subtle energetic body (etheric or pranic), we are in essence working on all the bodies. The treatments given here are for the etheric body.

VATA TREATMENTS

The method that I call "general cleansing" is the best method to harmonize and redistribute the pranas directly. This works primarily on the Udana Prana, the prana that controls the ascending movements and the Apana Prana that controls the descending movements of prana. It also works directly on the Vyana Prana, the prana that unites the body in all its aspects. This cleansing also opens the nadis and allows for free movement of the pranas throughout the bodies (see figure 16, page 150).

Repeat 3 times on front, back and the two sides.

Figure 16. General Cleansing.

After cleansing the patient, self-energizing with prana is necessary before transmitting prana to the other person. If done correctly, it is not only harmless for the practitioner, but actually beneficial. If done incorrectly, it will deplete the therapist's own prana. Study of pranic healing should be taken before proceeding with any of the following methods. Accumulation of prana is done by yogic breathing methods, and the instructions that follow are correspondingly given by breathing cycles. A cycle equals one inhalation and one exhalation. After accumulating extra prana, the following possibilities exist to balance vata (see figure 17).

Energetic cleansing equalizes all the pranas. This facilities the harmonizing of all three humors as all the pranas become harmonized. Cleansing also helps remove the pranic congestion that accumulates in specific regions of the body. For example, prolonged mental work will tend to congest prana in the head. General cleansing will dis-

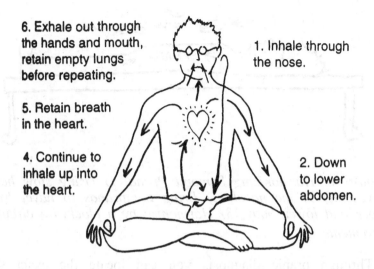

6. Exhale out through the hands and mouth, retain empty lungs before repeating.

5. Retain breath in the heart.

4. Continue to inhale up into the heart.

1. Inhale through the nose.

2. Down to lower abdomen.

3. Retain breath in abdomen for an instant.

Figure 17. Yogic breathing cycles.

perse this congestion, thus moving the humors back into their correct places—vata in the colon, pitta in the small intestine, and kapha in the stomach. Emotional congestion can happen in the intestines or the heart. Cleansing will start the process of balance by equalizing first the pranic congestion, then the humoral congestion.

Vata resides in the colon, therefore you can work directly on the energetic centers that control the large intestine. The location of these centers varies from person to person, however general areas can be given. The region of the pubic bone, the region below the navel, as well as the navel, correspond to the Apana Prana and vata. The navel is the site of the Samana Prana, which equalizes breathing and digestion. In order to harmonize vata, it is necessary to work on the Samana Prana, too (see figure 18, page 152).

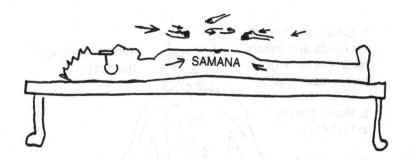

Figure 18. Harmonizing Samana Prana. 1) Using slow hand movements to the navel; 2) Bring the pranas to navel from upper and lower body; 3) Harmonize by a clockwise circular movement.

Through pranic diagnosis you can locate the exact site of imbalance pertaining to the vata humor. If this method is unfamiliar, then pulse diagnosis clearly reveals the site of aggravation in vata. If vata is aggravated, but still in the correct home area (colon area), then you may work directly on the first three centers mentioned above. This is done by cleansing the local area and then re-energizing the same area with prana collected by the therapist. This process is repeated three to five times until the pranic congestion is relieved.

It is not advised to take the pulse to see your progress once you have started the treatment. The pulse readings change once the person is lying down, thus they become an inaccurate way to compare. If the pranic treatments are done with the patient sitting, then it is possible to check periodically. However, my experience shows that it takes fifteen minutes or so for the energetic body to relay the full changes to pulse. Therefore, either use pranic diagnosis, or repeat cleansing and energizing for three cycles in each location needed according to the pulse. Then after the treatment and a few minutes' wait, the pulse can be taken again to verify the effectiveness.

For treatments of vata that are not located in the sites of vata, such as the lungs or stomach, efforts should be made to bring the vata down to its correct position. This is accomplished by general cleansing and then a local cleansing of the normal vata region. Follow this with an actual slow sweeping motion of the aggravated vata down to its home. This is done slowly and gently, like using a sponge on the kitchen counter. Slow, deliberate movements achieve clear results (see figure 19, page 154). This is accompanied by simultaneously giving prana. To harmonize this action, one hand should rest above the aggravated site and one hand should be centered in the normal vata site, just below the navel and above the pubic bone. Give prana. This has an equalizing and harmonizing effect between the aggravated site and the correct home site. Now more traditional Ayurvedic management methods should be used to maintain and keep vata from returning to an aggravated state.

Pranic congestion in the head—simple headaches—are often of vata origin. After general cleansing, the head can be worked on directly by using local cleansing. Actions that bring the prana downward are best; energizing should not be done unless one is able to pinpoint the exact location of the congestion and accompany it with energizing and cleansing. Usually, headaches are an imbalance of the prana located in the head. If sitting at a desk studying or working, this will also aggravate the Apana Prana and cause stagnation in the digestion, or hemorrhoids, constipation or other problems. In this case, the whole body should be treated to find if the apana is also disturbed and has imbalanced the head prana by excessive movement.

Nervous energy or nerve agitation should be treated by the Vyana Prana which controls nerve and muscle function. This prana is seated in the heart, but pervades the body equally. It has a special relation to the nervous system as a uniting force. All nervous problems affect the Vyana Prana. Start by general cleansing and then local cleansing on the heart area itself. This is a sensitive area, so it is best to approach it with care—even more so for the young or old. Harmony can be achieved by a very slow circular motion over the heart at a distance of approximately three inches from the physical body. The motions should

Figure 19. Moving vara to colon.

start clockwise and then be repeated counterclockwise for six full circles. Prana should be collected and projected during this energetic heart massage. This will have a harmonizing effect on the Vyana Prana (see figure 20). Further results can be achieved by placing your hands on the feet of the person and giving prana for eight to ten breathing cycles. If you know reflexology, then give prana to the solar plexus point. If not, then a foot massage with sesame seed oil is very effective in conjunction with pranic breathing. Full oil massages are recommended for nervous disorders. When these massages are given with prana, they become even more effective.

Constipation is generally of a vata origin. It can be treated by giving prana to the solar plexus, navel, and pubic areas. The emphasis should be on movement. This is accomplished by first cleansing locally, then charging the three mentioned areas. Next, start at the area of the small intestines and solar plexus, and visualize a white beam of prana coming out of two fingers. Use this beam to open the digestive tract, following the gastrointestinal tract down to the appendix, then up the ascending colon, across the transverse, and down the descending until the beam of prana passes out the anus. Repeat. This should be done in conjunction with stimulation of the Apana Prana and the Samana Prana and will produce results in twelve hours in

Figure 20. Harmonizing Vyana Prana.

most cases. The triphala formula should also be given in higher amounts if available. The liver should also be checked with one of the diagnostic methods mentioned in the previous chapter or by pranic detection.

PITTA TREATMENTS

Pitta is best controlled after harmonizing the pranas through general cleansing. Work first on vata as it is more effective because it controls pitta. By following the above guidelines for vata, and then moving to the site of pitta, you can achieve a more comprehensive treatment.

Pitta rests in the small intestine, and when it is aggravated it can move either up or down to disturb kapha or vata. This movement is actually accomplished by the Samana Prana that becomes aggravated. It aggravates the vata humor, causing the motion necessary to push pitta out of its home. Control of the Samana Prana, the equalizing prana, is the key to harmonizing the pitta humor.

After treating vata, address the navel center, the site of Samana Prana. First, cleanse locally and then re-energize with fresh prana for three to five breathing cycles. If you project lunar (or cooling) prana the samana will be pacified quicker. The emphasis is on cleansing. Pitta is hot; when aggravated this heat manifests as pranic congestion. Cooling, or lunar, prana is very effective in breaking up pitta congestions. Lunar prana is best collected and projected by visualizing cool, cold prana entering and leaving during the inhalation and exhalation of the breathing cycles (see figure 21).

For pitta-type fevers and infections, cleansing is the primary form of treatment in conjunction with projecting cool prana. General cleansing can lower a fever several degrees immediately. General cleansing should not be done more than three to four times or the patient could lose too much prana. Cooling prana should be projected after general cleansing. This is most effective if it is projected into the solar plexus area for three cycles, then to the navel area for four cycles. Cleanse locally and repeat again. This will help to balance the metabolism, lower heat, harmonize pitta, and bring the equalizing prana (Samana) into action. Now cooling, bitter, anti-pitta herbs can be administered with greater effect.

For localized pitta infections, local cleansing can be given along with cooling prana. Here again, cooling prana is projected to offset the high heat of pitta. Normally, projecting abundant amounts of cool prana will help accelerate the healing of infections. The emphasis is more on en-

Figure 21. Inhaling Lunar Prana and projecting Lunar Prana.

ergizing with cool prana than on cleansing, although cleansing is also needed.

In cases of pitta diarrhea, cooling prana in conjunction with inhibiting qualities should be given. This is accomplished by first cleansing locally the small intestines, the navel, and the pubic areas. Energizing can now proceed as per the method given for constipation in the vata section. In addition one should visualize the binding qualities of Vyana Prana, the prana that holds everything together. Just visualize the beam of prana binding instead of moving. Diarrhea is another form of constipation, and shows an imbalance of Samana and Apana Pranas.

In cases of low pitta, or of low agni, pranic healing can be very helpful. With low agni (the ability to digest) it is best to work directly on the solar plexus area. As in all cases, general cleansing helps as a primary step. After that, the solar plexus can be cleansed and charged with hot prana. Hot, heating, or solar prana is collected and projected by using visualization. The best method for visualizing is to actually "feel" the desired quality versus just "thinking" about it. If one only "thinks" about the visualization, it is 75 percent less effective unless one has done special study to develop this skill.

Likewise, low pitta can be raised by projecting hot prana into both the navel and solar plexus areas. Start by cleansing the solar plexus and then energizing it with hot prana for three to five cycles. Next, move to the navel area and cleanse and then energize for three to five cycles. Repeat the treatment to both areas twice.

KAPHA TREATMENTS

Kapha is best treated after both vata and pitta. General cleansing should be done in any case as it unblocks the congestion associated with kapha conditions. Physical kapha conditions relate to cold, congested pranic conditions, as one may guess.

For high kapha in the stomach area—its home—hot, cleaning prana should be projected. It is best in all the humors and in all kinds of pranic treatments, to follow the natural systems of the physical body. This is because, more often than not, the prana follows the same route. It is also easier and more efficient to aid the body in its natural routes than to try and force some concept on it.

Kapha will be easier to bring out through the digestive tract if it is accumulated in the stomach, or up through the mouth if it is located in the lungs. As kapha is usually associated with excess of some kind, it will have to leave the body through some route. It is unlikely that a pranic treatment would cause a person to vomit kapha excess—this would demonstrate an improper approach from the therapist—even though it is possible to stimulate Udana Prana to cause such an action. However, it is normal for the patient to cough up or defecate kaphagenic mucus after pranic treatments.

Treatments for the congestion of the stomach area should be performed after general cleansing and treatment of both vata and pitta. Start by local cleansing of the stomach area, then energize the stomach with hot prana for five to seven breathing cycles. Now move the hand down from the stomach area slowly—all the while giving prana—following the natural course of the intestinal tract; i.e., move your hand over the etheric small intestines, the etheric colon, and out. This will aid the natural movement of digestion, which will usually be sluggish because of the high kapha. For the accompanying constipation, use the treatment given in the section on vata (see figure 22, page 160).

Kapha congestion in the lungs can be treated with hot prana and local cleansing. Local cleansing should be performed several times to break up the pranic congestion in the lungs, and then the hot prana is projected. The quality of movement should be projected at the same time from the base of the lungs upward to the throat for five breathing cycles. Charge the throat for three breathing cycles and cleanse locally. Avoid the head area; do not bring congested prana into the head area. Bringing it into the throat is a natural function, as that is what the body will do sooner or later. Bringing it into the head can cause headaches and other secondary problems, so it should be avoided.

Kapha is best controlled by cleansing and energizing the pitta-related centers of the solar plexus and the navel. This will activate the pranas that will stimulate the actions of the pitta and vata humors. The Vyana Prana plays an important role in kapha accumulation. As it is the binding prana located in the heart, it has a special

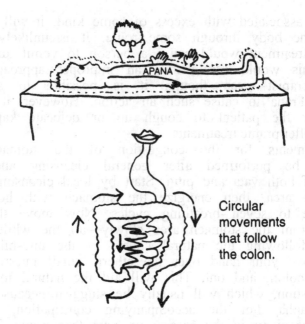

APANA

Circular
movements
that follow
the colon.

*Figure 22. Treating Apana Prana
for constipation.*

relationship to kapha. Care should be given to cleanse and stimulate the heart area whenever working on kapha related problems.

• • •

While these only represent a small number of possibilities in which pranic healing can be used to treat the three humors and their respective problems, it is enough to give an indication of the enormous possibilities available. The subject of pranic treatments in conjunction with more traditional Ayurvedic herbs and food treatments has not been covered here, as it is a complete study in itself. Readers should, however, also explore this area.

12

Sexual Rejuvenation Methods

❧ *Rama walked in front and Lakshmana followed in the rear,*
both conspicuous in their hermit's dress; and between the
two shone Sita, resplendent as Maya (the Divine Energy)
between the Absolute and the Individual Soul. ❧

Any book on healing that does not address the effects of sexuality—mentally and physically—and our health is incomplete. The following information is given in light of health and is not meant to offer any specific moral attitude, nor is it intended to offend any persons or groups. This information is provided to maintain or correct health problems, not to encourage or promote any special activity or method. Ayurveda has an abundant amount of information on how to maintain overall vitality by rejuvenating the sexual organs and how to best manage sexual energies.

> Day and night are nothing other than the Lord. Day is his prana and night is his substance. Those who indulge in passion in the day, waste away prana. Those that give play to passion in the night are as good as celibate.[1]

The Vedic sages were not negative to life. They often married and had families. Their families did not impair their spiritual lives or yogic attainments as so many people would have us believe. They also realized that the improper use of sexual energy wastes away prana and thus life. Overindulgence or improper use according to time of day and season wastes prana. The sages were aware of the

---

[1] Parsna Upanishad, ch. 1, verse 13, my transliteration.

correct use of the most powerful creative energy in humans—sexual energy. This sexual energy is none other than prana, our very life essence. Suppression or overuse of our basic life energy damages the fundamental connection to live and enjoy life. Misuse will also affect our ability to unite with pure consciousness. The deeper meaning of the quote at the beginning of this chapter is that "light" (or day) is the awakened state and "dark" (or night) is the state of ignorance.

SEX AND AYURVEDA

Rejuvenation formulas and aphrodisiac formulas are derived from two distinct branches of Ayurveda. Rejuvenation is used to increase the longevity of the whole body and mind. Aphrodisiacs are given to specifically rejuvenate the sexual organs and to provide healthy children. Of the eight branches of Ayurveda, these two branches are of special interest because they do not exist in such a developed state in the West.

> The therapy which creates potentiality for the getting of offspring for the maintenance of the continuity of the lineage, which causes instantaneous sexual excitation, to a degree that one is capable of indulging in sexual acts with women uninterrupted like a strong horse, and is exceedingly loved by women, which nourishes the tissue elements, by which even the signs of seminal debility do not appear in his body, which enable him to remain like a big tree having innumerable branches (family), and to earn respect from people by virtue of his having procreated several children, which is conducive to his enjoying happiness and eternity in this world and beyond (through his children), and which brings about longevity, beauty, strength and nourishment is known as aphrodisiac therapy.[2]

---

[2]Caraka Samhita, vol. III, R. K. Sharma and Bhagwan Dash, trans. (Varanasi, India: Chowkamba Sanskrit Series Office, 1992), pp. 8-9.

Ayurveda excels in aphrodisiac technology. This is not because the sages were obsessed with sex, but rather because of the political and economic implications. A stable country meant a good king and an easy succession to his heir. As the king was the patron of the medical arts, he footed the bills for herbal research and growing medicines. If the king had no heir, the political and social disruptions caused problems for the whole country and cut short the monthly pay check. For these reasons doctors studied carefully how to increase the fertility of both king and queen. During this long process they probably ran a lot of tests, which explains why they were married and had children (note: there is no historical evidence to this last reference!).

The Ayurvedic usage of the term "aphrodisiac" means the health of the sexual organs. It does not imply that one will get disproportionately excited by ingesting a special formula. What it does mean is that daily ingestion of certain plants and foods increases the sexual fluids and increases the vitality of those organs. Vitality means prana. Aphrodisiacs increase the likelihood of a healthy child and an increase in the enjoyment of the sexual act itself. Ayurveda states that the most effective aphrodisiac is an excited partner. Caraka says that all individual items are beautiful, but that a woman is the sum total of all beautiful things in nature. Thus women are considered to be the best aphrodisiacs.

This obviously shows wisdom. The emphasis is on beauty and an aroused partner, not on medicines. Although Ayurveda does have excellent formulas to combat impotence, debility, and infertility, the primary emphasis is on a mutually attractive sexual interest and one of beauty. Ayurveda may seem one-sided to women, as there are no references on what is the best aphrodisiac for women. I personally believe the primary aphrodisiac for women is love. Love is the uniting principle of the universe, and it offsets many of the side effects of poor sexual habits.

Ayurveda clearly states that certain preparations are necessary before using aphrodisiac formulas.

If a person take these aphrodisiac recipes in appropriate quantity and in proper time, when the channels of circulation of their body are clean, then they help in the promotion of virility, nourishment and strength. Therefore, depending on the strength of the person, elimination therapies should be administered to him, before he resorts to these aphrodisiac recipes. As a dirty cloth does not get properly colored (with die), similarly in an uncleaned body, the aphrodisiac recipes do not produce the desired effects.[3]

When prana is stagnant or blocked, sexual function is impaired. A sedentary lifestyle does not aid the circulation of prana; it directly causes stagnation and blockage with time. Food is also responsible for the congestion or blockage of prana over a period of time. A heavy, rich diet will cause pranic congestion. Modern research has linked prostate cancer in men to overly rich diets. Food in its most subtle state results in ojas. Additionally, our intake of liquid is also important for sexual function, as it is the liquid consumed that becomes prana in its subtle state.

Remember in chapter 10 we discussed the Ayurvedic system of the seven tissue levels of the body? Using the view that each level creates the next level we can see that the seventh or final level is the sum total of all bodily substances. The final transformation of what we eat and drink results in the reproductive fluids. They are the most refined and potent physical element in the body. The combination of the male and female fluids results in life; there is enormous potential in these fluids. As food and drink are refined, they move through the tissues from the first to the seventh level. With each level the food is becoming closer to ojas and the drink is becoming closer to prana. The reproductive fluids are highly concentrated ojas and prana (tejas also). It is these principles in combination with the sperm, ovum, and the soul that create life.

---

[3]Caraka Samhita, vol. Ill, p. 81.

As ojas relates to the essence of the kapha humor, so prana relates to the essence of the vata humor. Tejas is the essence of the pitta humor. Tejas in this context is the principle of transformation. The principle of cohesion, of stability, of protection all belong to ojas. Ojas is the basis of our immune response system. In a dangerous comparison of allopathic and Ayurvedic views, we can see that depletion of the marrow, which produces the white blood cells that fight infection, can lower our immune response. Ayurveda says that reproductive fluids are the outcome of the marrow, hence excessive loss of sexual fluids taxes the marrow and thus lowers the immune response and the strength of the body.

Overindulgence in fluid loss, for men and women, also affects the prana. It is actually the lower prana, the Apana Prana, that governs the exit of body wastes and sexual actions, including orgasm and ejaculation. If the apana is overexcited or overused, it imbalances the vata humor which it controls. Vata lives in the colon as does the apana. From an Ayurvedic point of view, too much sex will eventually cause vata-related diseases. For that matter, habitual colonics or enemas will also disrupt the apana and thus vata. Care should be given to harmonize the pranas or humors after intense sexual activity.

Ayurveda states that sexual activity should be limited to the genitals. There are a number of reasons for this that are not moralistic. Anal sex directly aggravates the apana and vata, even in moderate amounts. There are also hygienic problems associated with this type of interaction. The pranic balance of prana and apana is also disrupted. Prana is solar and apana is lunar; this yin-yang balance is disturbed by anal sex. However, there are things that can balance this activity if done occasionally. Sesame oil enemas with anti-vata herbs after sex will help. Each application should be done after a cleansing enema of warm water. This will help to harmonize the apana. One should consult an Ayurvedic doctor for constitutional management, as this causes other subtle imbalances in the body if habitual. After a period of rest (thirty to sixty minutes) mild exercise, such as walking, will help the body to harmonize the pranas. Anti-vata foods, namely kapha foods, should be taken. A calm environment promotes harmony in the five pranas and the three humors. Anal sex is best avoided as it is difficult to balance in the long run. Oral sex is far less disruptive to the pranas. The Apana Prana is not directly aggravated, and if orgasm is not the goal or the result, then the action is not disruptive to the humors. The mental or emotional excitement developed can overstimulate the mind, causing ejaculation much sooner in a man. If this is not desirable, then short periods of play are preferred, as they imbalance the pranas less. If a man and woman join together in oral sex simultaneously, a different polarity results.

Man is solar and woman is lunar. However, the genitals of the man are lunar (kapha-related semen) and the woman's genitals are solar (pitta-related). This is why there is such an attraction to the opposite sex—like seeks like. The solar man seeks to unite with the solar genitals of the woman and the lunar woman seeks to unite with the lunar genitals of the man. In oral sex a different kind of energetic polarity results due to the solar and lunar poles of the body. The man is solar orally as the woman is genital and vice versa. The mental and emotional stimulation is of an opposite quality than through normal intercourse. Energetically speaking, it is not a harmonizing act, it is stimulating, which is why it is exciting foreplay. The nonharmonizing factor is one reason why Ayurveda says not to have oral sex, and hygiene is no doubt another.

Self-gratification has a depleting effect on the body for four reasons. First is the actual loss of reproductive fluids; second, there is no opposite energy with which the pranas can balance, no polarity is created; third, there is no emotional exchange between partners that has a harmonizing effect on the pranas; lastly, in order to stimulate yourself, it is necessary to imagine a situation, person, or action. This act of imagination causes an imbalance between the prana that resides in the head and the Apana Prana that controls the sexual arousal of the genitals.

Habitual self-gratification causes a lowering of overall pranic vitality and debilitates the kidneys with time. The kidneys play a vital role in the creation of reproductive flu-ids, and if the emotional balance of a partner is not there to harmonize the pranas, the apana associated with the kidneys is disrupted. Frustration related to sex, accompa-nied with habitual self-gratification, is very depleting on all the apana functions and results in chronic vata imbalances.

Perhaps the aspect to be the most alert about is the overstimulation of the imagination. When alone this is needed for gratification. However, when you are with your partner, imagination creates blocks to a fully harmonious experience. In normal copulation the mutual emotional love and mutual physical stimulation are functioning nat-urally, thus balance results. If one of the partners is not present, but fantasizing, then the natural harmony is dis-rupted. Where the mind goes, the prana follows. This is a fundamental law of the universe; it just works like that. If you are thinking of the image that excites you in self-grati-fication while making love with your partner, harmony will not result. The experience will be less satisfying, even draining, because you were not present. Pranic harmony (which means ALL harmony) cannot occur if your prana and mind are not present in the action of making love.

The pranic relation to the mind explains why the sex-ual phenomenon is 95 percent mental. The Apana Prana is the prana that controls the sexual function for both men and women. It has a direct relationship with the control-ling prana of the brain. This controlling prana is seated in both the heart and the head. Together these two operate the mental and physical components that control the ac-tion of sexual arousal and intercourse. The very action of thinking is the movement of prana in consciousness. In fact, nothing takes place that is not 95 percent mental, be-cause that is just the movement of prana and mind to-gether. One factor that changes this natural process is love, another is meditation. Through either love or medita-tion the mental aspect of making love can be subdued or stopped naturally. This can rarely be cultivated, neverthe-less it can naturally happen in a deeply loving exchange.

Concerning sex, Ayurvedic counsels revolve mainly around the fertility of both partners and the child that results from the union, but some other points are also of interest to Westerners. It is said that aphrodisiacs should be taken on a regular basis if one has sexual relations, and that they should especially be taken before and after copulation. This is just common sense. We must use the optimum methods known to replenish the reproductive fluids that are lost or exchanged in intercourse. In fact there is a tremendous exchange of prana in lovemaking. Ayurveda categorically states that abstaining from sex is not healthy for normal people.

If a person keeps himself absolutely free from sexual intercourse, then this gives rise to mental stress. [4]

Aphrodisiacs should be taken with milk or ghee, as these two foods are considered to replenish reproductive fluids directly. Formulas should be taken in accord with the digestive capabilities of the individual. Don't drink four quarts of milk to replenish fluids if you don't have the ability to digest it. These substances should be taken warm (pitta) or hot (vata, kapha), never cold. Honey and raw sugar work immediately to carry the formula to the tissues, and honey, itself, is a natural aphrodisiac.

Sex performed at night is the least disruptive to the pranas; in other words, you lose less prana to your partner in the night. The winter is also considered to be the best season for sex; summer is the worst. In the winter kapha is the highest in nature, and as kapha controls the fluids of the body, sexual activity has the least depleting effect at this time of year. The high external temperatures of summer overheat the body and cause increased pitta, which in turn results in a lowering of kapha, which controls the sexual fluids. Refer to chapter 7, Table 6 (page 82) to see the times of day and season that each humor predomi-

---

[4]Caraka Samhita, vol. Ill, p. 72, commentary by Cakrapani Datta.

nates, in order to understand the logic behind these statements. When sex is done at "inappropriate" times, then aphrodisiac formulas are needed in higher doses.

INSIGHTS FOR WOMEN

The health of the female reproductive organs determines the health of the woman to a great extent. If this system is imbalanced it affects the whole body through the hormonal system. The hormones then affect the emotions and psychology of the woman. It is very important for a woman to learn what her options are in self-care. It is not normal for a woman to have painful menstruation and strong PMS symptoms. These problems can be corrected 90 percent of the time with herbs. If you are having, or have a history of, these kinds of problems, I strongly suggest that you find a woman health practitioner who can guide you in self-care with plants and herbs.

There are several Ayurvedic plants known for their effect on the female system. Two stand out as excellent. Shatavari is considered to be the primary aphrodisiac (remember this means health of the genitals) herb for women. The aloe family is considered to be the prime rejuvenator for women. Shatavari is Sanskrit for "possesses a hundred husbands." The Sanskrit name for aloe is kumari, or "young girl." Both of these herbs are described in chapter 8, but it is good to know that almost every aphrodisiac formula, for men or women, includes shatavari. In brief, it is necessary to use shatavari for a minimum of three cycles and aloe for two before achieving results. Shatavari contains many beneficial plant hormones in very small doses that correct imbalances over a period of time. It is said that most women can take shatavari for their whole lives, aiding any problems with PMS, childbirth, menopause, and other smaller problems that relate to the female cycle.

It became apparent the moment that I began to write this section that I was not qualified to write anything about female sexuality because I am a man. This obviously limits my ability to offer any significant insights to women interested in sexuality from an Ayurvedic or spiritual point of view. With this in mind, I asked a woman to write her experience of sexuality and any insights that may be of value for other women. The following was written in hopes that her experiences may help other women searching for a greater understanding and fulfillment of their own sexuality.

> When I was younger I didn't enjoy sex; not that I was frigid, on the contrary I was very sensual and enjoyed sexual contact. However, once penetration began I ceased to feel anything. Psychologists would have considered me as a clitoral type rather than a vaginal type. I suffered a lot from the fact that I never had an orgasm while making love. It was especially hard because at that time I was married and deeply loved my husband with whom I had two beautiful children.
>
> Then one day I started reading a book that I had purchased five years earlier, the year I met my husband. The book was called *The Function of Orgasm* by Wilhelm Reich; this book changed my life. I do not remember precisely what he said in this book, but once I had finished reading it, I was so impressed that I became determined to find some way to be able to live and enjoy that energy released by orgasm. I remember even saying to myself that I didn't want to die before experiencing what Wilhelm Reich was talking about, it sounded so grandiose.
>
> A few months later I met a girl who became my best friend and she lent me a book on bioenergetics by Lowen. I read it and decided that I should start working in bioenergetics as I felt that it was a direct application of Reich's ideas. That was the beginning of a new life for me because I began to participate in therapy groups. The first group I did was on bioenergetics, then one in rebirthing, followed by many other kinds of therapy. Through them I was determined to find that treasure called orgasm. I won't go into details about those processes, but one thing is important to mention about them. Soon after starting those different therapies I became interested in the spiritual path. For this I am ever grateful.

As the work on myself proceeded, my sex life improved, and I began to enjoy making love, although it was still nothing of the sort that I had read about in Reich's book. During this time I began learning from a spiritual teacher who often referred to sexuality as a gateway to consciousness. My teacher also said many times that men were often making love in the same way that they sneeze, as a release of energy. He stated that lovemaking was a communion with your partner and the whole cosmos. He said that women were able to have multiple orgasms if they were not repressed psychologically, and if their partner could prolong ejaculation.

I had already started practicing meditation, and these statements rang a bell in me; they were very close to what I had read years before in Wilhelm Reich's book. I began to ask several women friends of their personal experiences to know if they had multiple orgasms; none of them did. I continued to follow my teacher's advice regarding therapies, active meditations, breathing exercises, and dance. Many of these activities were incorporated into two methods. These methods began to clear and open the energetic channels in my body. This allowed the energy to move freely throughout my body and to stimulate the major centers of the body. As my sexual enjoyment improved, I forgot about it, and concentrated the next few years on my spiritual search. I pifxticed other meditations to clear my mind of its numerous thoughts, and to find out who I was.

My neurosis was fading away with the work I was doing and I became more relaxed, enjoyed dancing a lot, and the spontaneity of childhood came back. At this time my teacher died and I heard of another realized man, a disciple of Sri Ramana Maharishi, living in the north of India. At the first opportunity I traveled there to meet him.

On my second day of being in his presence my mind blew up completely, a current of energy started vibrating at the base of my spine, then rose up along my back. An immense joy and laughter took hold of me—so much laughter! At the same time my mind was empty. It was funny because there was so much laughter, but I was not the one controlling the laughing. I was only witnessing the laughter. I found out after some time of staying near this man that I had been in touch with my own Self.

After this experience I began to feel my body differently. I became even more receptive to other people. Sometimes I would feel a very strong sexual attraction in the presence of a male friend of mine. It was amazing to feel such a powerful energy, especially because we were just friends. Previously, while participating in a therapy group on death, I had felt this same kind of intense energy with my boy friend of the time. It was as if our outer bodies were making love when we were close to each other, without even touching. At the time of that therapy group, I took this experience to be just part of the therapeutic process, never realizing that it could be our natural state. Especially that the experience ended after the group finished. However, I now began to experience this again and I was not in any kind of therapy situation. I was simply sitting in the presence of a Self-realized man. Through sitting with him I came into contact with my own inner source.

When I met my current companion I realized that my sexuality had been completely transformed. Orgasm was no longer a release of energy; on the contrary, it became an opening to more and more energy, pleasure, and orgasms. Orgasms became multiple and lovemaking became an endless delight. Without any effort, or special position, or any mental stimulation, sex became an endless pleasure. During lovemaking the orgasms are rising on their own, one after the other, and in between are spaces of deep pleasure. The more I have orgasms, the deeper and more intense they become, and the more ecstatic I become. I come out of lovemaking with a deep well-being, gratitude, and profound relaxation.

My companion masters his sexual energy and knows how to prolong pleasure without ejaculating too quickly. When we make love for long periods of time, an hour or more, it allows my body to become more and more orgasmic. My body becomes so sensitive that each cell becomes orgasmic—there is no more separation within my own body—nor with my companion. Tfye more I am aroused during intercourse, the stronger the orgasms are, they start as waves rising and falling within my vagina and spread through my whole body. It is very different than a clitoris orgasm. Generally when the clitoris is stimulated to orgasm, the pleasure ends with that climax, preventing a vaginal orgasm from occurring. However, if the clitoris is stimulated not to orgasm, the pleasure becomes more intense and profound during lovemaking, leading to multiple vaginal orgasms. We very often reach this state of total ecstasy when we make love with a peaceful mind. It is true that if we are worried, we don't reach such a profound quality of union. And if we are anxious we can't even make love, as we are not in the mood. The quality of the mind is the most important. The more peaceful the mind, the better quality sex. My spiritual search has been the best help to develop a peaceful mind. What began as a search for orgasm became an inner spiritual union with my own Self.

INSIGHTS FOR MEN

The upsurge in prostate problems and cancer in men has been linked, among other things, to poor diet. Poor diet is processed foods, rich fried foods, excessive amounts of meat, and a diet overly rich in protein. As a culture, we are obsessed with protein. This is bizarre given the fact that most decathlon participants are vegetarian. Arnold Schwarzenegger won Mr. World with a low protein vegetarian diet. There is ample medical proof to show that people live longer on low protein vegetarian diets. If you are suffering from, or feel you may be prone to, prostate problems, I strongly suggest that you change your diet immediately before undertaking other forms of treatment.

A small change in diet can be accompanied by regular exercise. Reduce stress in your life as much as possible. You can also do a simple exercise every day that will help. Contract the muscles that lift your testicles. Experiment several times; there is a slight difference between contracting the muscles around the anus and the ones that lift your testicles. Start by contracting these muscles five times three to four times per day. After one week contract them ten times in a row, three to four times per day. This simple method exercises the prostate directly. The prostate is a muscular gland that you can build up slowly with exercise. I regularly use this exercise at my desk because I spend hours sitting and writing at the computer. Hours of sitting year after year cause the deterioration of this gland, especially when accompanied by a poor diet.

There are many very good herbs in India for the rejuvenation of the male sexual organs. The most famous for men are ashwagandha, kaunch, shilajit and shatavari. Studies show that ashwagandha and shatavari mixed together increase the erection of the male organ (see shatavari in chapter 8). These herbs are very effective if taken for a period of several months, although it is possible to achieve results within a few days. However, more important than any herbal supplement is your mental outlook and approach to sex.

Orgasm for a man is controlled by the mind. This is a far-reaching statement. It is not simplistic, nor is it onesided; it is factual. When I first heard of this idea, I received it with mixed feelings. In one way I was happy to know that I could control the time of ejaculation with a thought, and on the other hand, why should I interfere with my natural urges? In fact, the practical application proved very difficult, and I was often left wondering about the validity of this idea. For over twenty years I have tried many different methods of control and different ways to create a stronger bond with my partner through sex. The conclusions that I came to are that the mind does control ejaculatipn, and that methods used to control ejaculation activate the mental process, thus preventing a natural loving exchange between partners during intercourse. Mind and love are not synonymous. If one is there the other is not.

The best lovemaking happens in a nonthinking circumstance. As stated earlier, where the mind goes the prana goes. If you are thinking about control or something else while making love it actually blocks the natural circulation of prana between the partners. Mental control equals pranic control. I intuitively did not like this kind of imposed mental control in this beautiful moment of being with my companion. However, I would often ejaculate very quickly, especially if it had been a long time between love-making. Still I felt that the time together was very special, a moment that mind should not be involved, for it is a moment of pure sensuality, of sensations, of bonding, of feeling, of love. What business did the mind have coming into this moment?

The answer for me, and of course it is personal, lies between a firm decision not to ejaculate quickly before I start to make love and a simple physical method that requires nothing but awareness of when ejaculation is going to happen. Between these two simple methods I am able to enjoy lovemaking as often as my partner and I wish to make love, and for as long as we wish. The mind is controlled by—and controls—the prana. The prana controls ejaculation. By a clear decision in the mind, the pranas are controlled; this means ejaculation is retarded or suspended until one wishes. Mental control is that easy; just a firm decision and enjoy. It helps if one puts the emphasis on prolonging pleasure, rather than on some imposition by an idea or concept that, "I have to last longer, ugh!" There is nothing wrong with just wishing to enjoy, and helping your partner to enjoy, the pleasure of bonding for a longer period of time.

The simple method that I use when I get overly excited and feel that I am about to ejaculate is to withdraw until only the tip of the penis is still in the vagina. I then wait a few moments until I feel the urge to ejaculate subside. One may also withdraw completely and play around in other ways before entering again. One must be aware that withholding ejaculation can be harmful if care is not taken to prevent an excessive buildup of sperm/prana. If this happens, in other words if you feel a block or pressure in the penis or prostate, finish the session with ejaculation—especially if any tension is felt in the region of the perineum. If the urge to ejaculate never arises, then everything is fine also. My experience is that the more I make love, the less desire I have to ejaculate.

Ayurveda states that the suppression of the urge to ejaculate causes pain in the penis and testicles, depression, cardiac pain, and retention of urine. Warm baths,

massage, wine, chicken, milk, enemas, and intercourse are
prescribed to correct the problem. Retention of semen can
be very beneficial if done correctly, and damaging if done
incorrectly, especially for the prostate gland. For a correct
method see Mantak Chia's book on male sexuality.[5] This
method describes pranic exercises to circulate the prana,
thus preventing the damaging secondary effects of seminal
retention. This method requires years of practice, and is
best leaned from a teacher, as permanent damage can result from the improper application. I do not recommend
this kind of method as I know several men who have dam-
aged themselves by using it. Mr. Chia's method is good
and it does work. However, you should not try it alone.
There are too many variables in the human body and a
book does not account for your individuality—one method
is not going to fit all people. If this method attracts you,
then learn it from him or one of his qualified students.

If you are having problems because of impotency or
premature ejaculation, I suggest the following steps: eliminate stress as much as possible from your life; change your
diet; and use a combination of the herbs listed for men in
this section. Stress is a killer. It disturbs the prana in the
mind, which then affects the Apana Prana in the pubic region, thus inhibiting sexual function. Meditation is very
helpful to help relax the mind and enhance the normal
functions. Physical exercise is critical, as are the dietary
guides given for the prostate gland. At first a diet that lowers toxins (see chapter 14) is advised for several weeks, followed by a low protein diet according to your constitution.
This should be accompanied by ashwagandha and shatavari (and warm milk or ghee) at a dose of 6 grams per day
taken with meals (2 grams with each meal).

One should also be aware that the excessive loss of
seminal fluid depletes the body and lowers ojas. Ojas is
the most subtle essence of our food, as prana is of liquids.

---

[5]Mantak Chia, *Taoist Secrets of Love: Cultivating Male Sexual Energy*
(Santa Fe, NM: Aurora Press, 1984).

Too many orgasms over a short time deplete the body of both, leaving one open to disease and fatigue. What is excessive? This is open to debate. Ultimately one must decide from personal experience. Ayurveda gives these guidelines: vata people have the least stamina, so should ejaculate the least; pitta people are average in stamina; and kapha people have the greatest capacity for ejaculation. In my experience this is not really a problem for the average person; sexual exchanges are ever-changing from day to day, season to season, and year to year. Like any season, things are always in change. If you feel tired after sex, then use more of the aphrodisiacs suggested.

PERSONAL INSIGHTS

I would like to try and clarify some points about sex for people interested in meditation and a spiritually harmonious way of life. The following are my own opinions and do not necessarily reflect the traditional views. I personally feel that some basic misunderstandings exist for the average student.

While most teachers or spiritual groups advocate celibacy or abstinence from intercourse, it may not necessarily be in keeping with spiritual development. I will absolutely agree with abstinence for people practicing Kundalini Yoga or yogas involving the manipulation of the pranas. This and a satvic diet are necessary. These practices must be accompanied by a teacher who watches your progress, who provides an undisturbed place to live, and who can provide the emotional support necessary to replace the emotional void left by sexual abstinence.

In the above situation when a teacher provides the emotional support, it is possible to abstain from sexual relationships without creating an imbalance of some kind. People who are alone, and who concentrate totally on their practice, are also not included in the following discussion, provided that they arrived there naturally and effortlessly. Another exempt category is mature people in the later stages of life. It is normal with age, or maturity, to lose

interest in sex, and it is actually a sign of health, not imbalance. There is another small category of people who are
just not interested in sex; if these people live alone or with
someone of a like mind, then it can be okay. However, if
you live with a partner and one of you is interested and
the other not, then imbalance will result. This creates
mental and physical tensions which led to disharmony in
the humors (hence the expression "bad humored!").

For the vast majority of people, sex is a natural function of the body and is necessary for proper health. This
section is directed to these people. Forced abstinence can
cause a number of problems ranging from mental depression to physical blocks that result in illness. Making love
stimulates and activates the five pranas. Their regular activation plays a vital role in keeping the nadis open and
clear throughout the body. It is a very complete form of exercise and more fun than most sports! Sex relieves tension
and stress through a natural activation of the pranas,
which in turn causes the body to expel toxins from the tissues. If done according to your individual capacity, there is
nothing healthier.

People are often asked to refrain from sex or from orgasm when associated with teachers or spiritual teachings. This is only healthy for a very few mature people. It
is the mind that must be addressed, not the body. To replace one concept with another is not an improvement;
eliminating all concepts is the real Brahmarcharya. If this
is done, celibacy will naturally happen. In regard to this
kind of unhealthy practice I would like to recount a story
that my teacher told publicly some years ago.

"Poonjaji had heard of one man who had walked to
heaven from the Himalayas (Yudhishtara, brother of Ar-
juna). Legend gave the exact route that this man had
taken with six other people in his family, but he was the
only one to complete the journey because of his inner purity. Consequently my teacher, Poonjaji, started to walk
the same route. Several days went by; he had left the
plains and lower mountains behind and was now climbing
in the high mountains. He had no warm clothes as he lived
in the plains and was concerned with heaven, not comfort.

At night he would ask to stay with sadhus (holy men who live alone doing austerities or penance). One night he begged lodging from a sadhu. He was fed and given a bed in the cave, which was a blanket on a stone ledge and a sand pillow. Here at the height of the Himalayas, above tree line, frozen, lived this man who practiced austerities alone in silence. This sadhu had no possessions other than a pot in which to cook and drink from. Poonjaji decided he didn't need the sand pillow so he moved it on to the floor and found a pornographic girlie magazine under it!"

"Poonjaji's comment was, 'it is better to have a girl under the arm than under the head!' The sadhu had left physical relationships behind, but not the mental attachments. The actual definition of Brahmacharya, which people normally equate with celibacy, is to only reflect on the unchanging substratum, Consciousness." Vasistha says this:

> By the practice of brahmacharya (mental continence or whole-souled devotion to Brahman), courage and endurance, and dispassion, and by intelligent practice based on common-sense, onfe obtains that which one seeks to obtain—self-knowledge. [6]

This is said not to give permission to overindulge in sex, but to clarify a much-confused subject. There is, in fact, no controversy regarding sexuality in so far as our experience of pure consciousness. Everything issues from the substratum of consciousness including the prana that manifests as sexual energy. *What is very important is our mental attitude toward sex.* It is the mind that unbalances the prana and so the humors. If the mind is obsessed with sex or food, it says something about the mind, and not the object of obsession. The only argument against sexual relations in terms of the religious-oriented person is in advanced practice of Jnana Yoga (Advaita), and yogas that

---

[6] *Yoga Vasistha: The Supreme Yoga,* vol. I, Swami Venkatesananda, trans. (Shivanandanagar, India: The Divine Life Society, 1991), p. 209.

manipulate the pranas directly, and I have already acknowledged that exception. If one cuts off or represses
one's sexuality, one cuts off the life force, prana, whose
natural function is to unite with the opposite polarity. To
a major degree, such a cut affects the relationship to life
itself.

To finish the story: "Poonjaji went on for some distance further until he came to a saddle in the glaciers.
There he met a man and a woman who looked like Shiva
and Paravati (Shiva is one of the Hindu trinity of Gods, he
represents meditation, austerities, destruction, and pure
Consciousness; Paravati is his wife). The woman came to
him and invited him to eat with them; she was incredibly
beautiful. The man remained silent as a stone; they were
both very luminous. They ate a grain mixed with honey
that Poonjaji described as 'incredibly delicious.'After some
time he left and returned down the mountains, feeling
that the Gods had come to him so now there was no need
for him to go to heaven. Was it a vision? Perhaps, except
that in India people eat with their hands, and Poonjaji's
hands smelled of Paravati's food for years after this
meeting."

Poonjaji had a wife and has two children. While he
spent much of his life alone in the pursuit of self-knowledge, he attributes this to ignorance rather than to necessity. His teacher, Sri Ramana Maharishi told people with
families to return home, that their desire to know God was
not in any way impaired by living a normal family life.
The realized teacher Sri Nasargadatta Maharaj lived in
Bombay with his family and often said the only important
factor was mental abstinence from desire toward anything, not only sex.

The fact of the matter is that as long as the five states
of matter, the five elements, are combined with prana, the
body exists, and the personality exists. As long as the body
exists, it will want to eat, drink, and have sex. Nothing
could be more natural or the cause of so much misunder-
standing. To sum it up: it is our mental attitude that determines if something is an obstacle, not the object or action itself. If our development is sufficient, the desire will

not be there anyway, and the question is moot. My experience is that if sex is available, I seldom want it or think of
it. However, if it is not available, I want it all the time and
think of it often. *This is the nature of the mind, not of
human sexuality.*

There are several different ways in which to regulate
the pranas in the actual act of making love. One is for the
man to withhold ejaculation, or sometimes both partners
can do this, and the other is to simply prolong the time period of being together.

For the first method, two popular schools exist. The
first one involves non-movement by either partner. The
couple simply unites and then remains together for an
hour or more. If done correctly, a natural current of prana
begins to circulate between the couple. This method is
very effective to break sexual tensions between a couple. If
a couple can repeat this passive intercourse, then slowly
the mental tensions and conditioning around sex will dis-
perse. The first dozen times can (and usually does) trigger
strong emotional reactions from both partners. These
must be seen for what they are, emotional releases of sexual vasanas, and not allowed to stop or interfere with the
process. This method is mostly therapeutic and does lead
to a stressless lovemaking in time. It is, however, not advised for the majority of people as a lifetime method. It can
cause pranic congestion in both partners, and men may
have a difficulty with the prostate gland if this method is
followed for longer than six months to a year. It is very
beneficial for couples to try for several months, as it places
the emphasis on being together in a loving way rather
than on peak orgasms. Keep in mind that this method
should be practiced for a period of time—one time is not
enough.

The other method that involves nonejaculation consists of physical and mental exercises to withhold the peak
orgasm. This allows a different kind of orgasm to happen—what is commonly called a "valley orgasm." This
method may be better for long-term use, provided it is
done correctly, because it involves physical exercises that
circulate the prana and transform its normal function into

a regeneration method, or a method to build up ojas for spiritual practices. This method is very well explained by Mantak Chia [7] in his books on male and female sexuality. However, as I said earlier, it is better to learn directly from him than from a book. These books are the most complete on the subject that I have found and are recommended for people interested in preserving their sexual fluids for rejuvenation, or for yogic practices. I do know people who have become impotent from these Taoist methods. I strongly suggest finding and following a qualified teacher if these types of methods are chosen. They are generally more dangerous for men than women.

The other option from the perspective of health and enjoyment is to prolong the experience as long as desired before orgasm. This also creates the possibility for valley orgasms, usually more for a woman than a man, but this depends on how often a couple make love. The simplest way to prolong the time, which allows for more enjoyment and a deeper emotional bonding, is for the man to withdraw and wait before continuing. Women need time to warm up. It is much more bonding and nourishing for both partners if the man can facilitate this period of warming up. Whatever happens for a couple, the primary result should be joy and a mutual appreciation of each other, not the perfection of a technique. Appreciation, love, and a deep contentment show that a positive emotional bonding has taken place, thus the pranas will be in harmony. Love is a necessary ingredient for . the lasting harmony of the prana and so the soul.

---

[7]Mantak Chia, *Taoist Secrets of Love: Cultivating Male Sexual Energy* (Santa Fe, NM: Aurora Press, 1984); and *Healing Love through the Tao: Cultivating Female Sexual Energy* (Jim Thorpe, PA: Healing Tao Books, 1986).

13
Psychology and Meditation

❖ There is no real difference between the ways of faith and those
of knowledge, for both are equally efficacious in putting
an and to the torments of birth and death. ❖

One of the most important factors in health is our mental
outlook. Our mental outlook directly affects the prana and
thus the three humors. Personally, it became obvious that
to recover my health I needed to make both minor and
major changes in my life. My experience has taught me
that the subtle changes I made in the mental process were
the most critical. These different perceptions helped me to
later initiate the major changes in my daily life. Without
these subtle changes in my views and attitudes, the healing process in my body could not have started.

The thoughts that we dwell on—that we establish relations with—are the thoughts that create our mental outlook. We slowly develop mental habits that in turn create
emotional, psychological, and physical habits, or vasanas.
Our life then becomes dominated by these mental conditionings. By changing the mental habits we can effect a
change on the other physical or emotional habits. This
does not happen overnight. We have acquired these habits
over a lifetime, and we need to make a prolonged, concentrated effort to change them. However, we can change, and
if I can do it, so can you.

The first mental habit that I needed to change was to
stop thinking negatively about my body, or the lack of self-
love. I had the tendency to ether ignore my body or to fight
against it. Once I was able to accept what was actually
happening to my body, things began to change. That
means that when I had back pain I accepted it. I didn't

wish it different, it was just there. Now I could take the correct measures to help correct the imbalance or pain. This acceptance of the reality of my body, this self-love, is the first great lesson that I learned about healing.

Once accepted—then changed: the body can start to heal itself more effectively with a little help from its friend—the mind. A positive, accepting attitude does miracles toward healing one's self. Once I stopped fighting the reality of my body's condition, then healing could proceed from the root. The mind is the root of our illness and diseases. As stated in chapter 1, mind is a combination of vasanas and prana.

True, not all diseases come from bad mental habits. However, how we view the accident, hereditary disease, viral infection, or other cause will be the root of healing ourselves. Therefore, we can say that the mind is the first place to start from; it is the root of healing ourselves.

Traditionally, Ayurveda recognizes that the mind, or our mental constitution, is dominant over our physical constitution. People have done amazing things through will power alone. Few of us have developed our will power to the extent that we can cure ourselves (though some have managed to kill themselves!) through mind alone. Yet, the possibility does exist. What today is termed "spontaneous remission" is often a very firm decision to get healthy again.

Not only is the role of the mind often neglected in allopathic or Western medicine, it is also neglected by the majority of Ayurvedic doctors as well. My personal experience in India was disappointing in this regard. Too many Ayurvedic practitioners are now following the Western way of treating the body. This superficial division doesn't work anywhere in the world—East or West. The very beauty of Ayurveda in today's world is that it never created false divisions in people. It never viewed the human being as a machine. Mind, feelings and emotions are impossible to separate from the body. All operate together to form a human being. Ayurveda not only understands the classic disease patterns of the mind, it was the first to document them thoroughly.

AYURVEDIC PSYCHOLOGY

Remember, the mind is a combination of the vasanas (mental impressions) and prana. Here are the therapeutic methods that Ayurveda uses to correct destructive mental patterns:

Meditation (control of the mind directly);
Breathing (control of the prana directly);
Sound (harmonizing the prana);
Prayer (harmonizing the mind);
Visualization (harmonizing the mind and prana together);
Herbs (controlling the prana with other qualities of prana);
Pranic healing (harmonizing the prana directly);
Gems (harmonize the cosmic pranas).

Why should we use the methods handed down from over 5000 years ago when they are available as modern methods? The primary reason is that the interrelationship between these therapies is not fully understood yet in the West. When used together in conjunction with a correct life style and diet, the results are indeed impressive. Yet, when used without a change in life style or diet, it reduces the effects by at least 50 percent. The common link in all of these methods is the prana that unites them. The ancient seers were the first people to develop such a complete range of complementary methods to achieve mental balance. This is due to their complete understanding of prana and its source, pure consciousness. They still are the only people to provide the basis for a *totally comprehensive system.* For example, Tibetan medicine is from Vedic sources and Chinese medicine lacks the spiritual dimension and how it relates to herbs, foods, and animals.

Ayurveda and Yoga are sister sciences that were developed by the same group of sages in the Himalayas. They often overlap with treatments and recommendations. The systems of psychology developed by the sages of Ayurveda and Yoga are more complete than Western psychology for three reasons: 1) they have been at it much longer; 2) they understand the effects of subtle energies (prana) on both the mind and the body; and 3) they could view the mental workings of the mind from a transcendental state.

When I speak of Yoga, I do not mean the method of different postures. Those methods actually fall under Ayurveda which literally means "how to live correctly." Ayurveda is more concerned with the health of the physical body. Yoga is more concerned with the spiritual union of human and god or the cosmos. Yoga means union. The two systems do recognize and help each other. It is very difficult to be interested in spiritual affairs if you are sick, dying, or wasted from overindulgence. Ayurveda is a system that maintains and promotes health so human beings can devote themselves, at the proper time, to finding their true nature.

The psychologies of both Yoga and Ayurveda perceive the cosmos as "not different" than we are. Each human being is a mini-universe living within the greater universe. The universe is comprised of both seen and unseen forces that function in an intelligent manner. The human body is also comprised of the same forces, both seen and unseen. These unseen forces are the aspects of prana and are described as three mental qualities: intelligence, action, and inertia (satva, rajas and tamas). The basic mental quality is pure intelligence (satva). Mind exists in that pure intelligence as movement of thought, which stimulates the vasanas and action (rajas). Laziness, lethargy, sleep, and inaction represent the third force of inertia (tamas).

Our psychological state is a play of these three qualities. The mental outlook is healthy when satva is predominant. When rajas predominates, mental and emotional disturbances arise. When tamas is predominant, the mentality is depressed, dull, and perverse. Thus the basis of psychology can be understood by seeing which of these qualities is predominant in the personality of the person at any given time. Ayurveda and Yoga work on lowering inertia and raising the purity of intelligence in the mind through action.

While this may seem simplistic, it is easily observable in both nature and people. All material substances and events promote one of the three qualities. Whatever we absorb in our minds either increases purity, disturbance, or resistance. If we start to see which activities help to increase our peace of mind, then we can increase them. When we recognize which activities increase disturbances, we can reduce them. Lastly, when those things which block the other two, or inhibit them, occur, we should eliminate them altogether.

An Example

I should say that at the time of this writing I had lived in India for roughly six out of the last ten years. I visited a number of doctors of diverse traditions. I was attracted to India for purely personal reasons. I became interested in healing through a personal experience that changed my health and thereby my life.

I have a deformation of the spine commonly known as kyphoscoliosis. Nothing serious, just a constant pain in my back. Sometimes it was a dull ache and at other times it was disabling. Imagine my surprise when after three sessions with a therapist the pain vanished for the first time in fifteen years! Even more surprising was that the therapist was Japanese, and used a very ancient pranic healing method. This resulted in my learning pranic healing, first from him and then another teacher. The method centered on using the life force to balance and invigorate the energetic system of the body, much like the Chinese system of acupuncture. I have explained this method in detail in my previous book, *Prana: The Secret of Yogic Healing.*

It was not until 1991, when I began to seriously research the traditional roots of using prana to heal, that I came across ancient references to Ayurveda. Living in India I had come across Ayurvedic doctors and medicines many times, finding most of the medicines to be very effective. I would sometimes visit the Ayurvedic pharmacy to buy certain herbal products that I liked. However, I had never been interested in learning more; I had the impression that it was a bit arcane. Nonetheless, through my research I became interested in learning more. It also became clear that pranic healing was limited with certain diseases and needed dietary and herbal supports to further aid the prana and thus the healing process.

At that time I was in and had been—aside from back pain—in good health for my whole life. What followed that year on my return to Europe was nearly fatal. After leaving India I decided to move to the south of France. For seven years I had primarily lived in India, leaving only to work and renew my visa. This was to be my re-entry into Western society. The transition went smoothly at first, but became more and more difficult as time passed, for cultural shock set in, and my financial reserves disappeared. The importance of my mental outlook in relation to my health became very meaningful over the next year.

As I described in the introduction I failed to either change my external situation or my mental attitudes. Thus, I continued to ignore my body. The result was that I almost bled to death and ended up in the hospital on an IV.

The competitive society and the increased action necessary to live in it stimulated the rajas or active mental principle. With the increase of action, satva, or pure quality of intelligence became less prominent. Times of tamas or inertia became much more common in the form of pain and depression. Combined with a pitta constitution I was in a perfect position to manifest an ulcer, a typical pitta illness. Pitta people also have a special relation to action or rajas as they are normally goal-oriented people.

The practice of anti-pitta food regimens and life style not only accelerated the healing of the ulcer, but completely eliminated the possibility of a relapse. The herb amla and large doses of Chavana Prash were the major supplements used, although shatavari is what I currently use daily, along with triphala, to manage pitta and prevent another relapse— especially in times of stress. In this somewhat embarrassing personal example several things are apparent:

1) Self-love is necessary to prevent and to cure disease;
2) Overactivation of rajas (action) or tamas (inertia) causes the mind to imbalance which then affects the three humors;
3) Measures to increase satva (harmony or pure mind) are necessary to lower action and inertia, thereby preventing mental imbalance;
4) Change external situations when possible, or if that is not possible, then change your relationship to the external situation;
5) Use Ayurvedic daily regimens for your constitution to maintain balance and harmony in the body.

MEDITATION

Rather than spending years analyzing mental qualities and habits, Yoga and Ayurveda give us practical instructions on how to change them. The foremost of these methods is meditation. At first fifteen to sixty minutes daily are needed to maintain the equilibrium of the mind. This should be eliminated as soon as possible to achieve a twenty-four-hour frame of mind. Too many schools or teachers use meditation as a symptomatic pill. It is not sufficient to sit for thirty minutes watching your breath and then start yelling at your husband or wife an hour later. &ome confusion exists between exercises and meditation.

In the personal example given above, it is apparent that even though I was meditating for many years, it was not sufficient to prevent mental imbalance and thus physical imbalance. In hindsight it is clear (as things usually are) that I had not transformed the exercises into an ever-present reality, or true meditation.

Meditation is a state of being, actually it is Being. An exercise is something to achieve something else— like peace. Meditation is beginningless and endless being.

Another way to say this is that meditation, as used in ancient Vedic scriptures, means to be Consciousness, or to identify yourself as the substratum of existence—God. Exercises are very good for calming the pranas and the mind, but they do not result directly in a re-identification of the person to the ultimate—which is the true meaning of meditation. Concentrating on the breath, on an object, using a mantra, chanting, or prayer are all good methods to bring a peaceful quality of mind and to harmonize the pranas. Although these methods bring results in a limited way, they do not bring lasting peace, which is defined as the unchanging reality. That which does not change is peace, because it is the substratum for everything else.

All exercises are helpful. However, the best medicine is a complete re-identification to the unchanging substratum. Most people acknowledge that exercises are needed at first to allow the mind to be able to use the most direct methods of re-identification. Both the indirect and direct methods are given below. As my personal experience illustrates, sooner or later the direct method must be used to recognize the fact that the substratum is always present (hence "substratum") and to know that I am not different from that substratum. This is a twenty-four-hour phenomenon, it is not possible to get out of it, or not know it, as it is with an exercise or practice.

Exercises in this context are defined as putting yourself outside of the "current of thoughts" that we call the mind. There are two basic methods to do this. The first is to follow the breath in and out of the mouth or nose, all the time placing the attention on the two spaces between the inhalation and exhalation. The second is to perceive that the current of thoughts is actually a series of single thoughts appearing separately. Recognizing this, one can place the attention on the spaces between the thoughts. Either of these two methods will result in calming the mind, one by the prana and the other by using the mind.

It is usually difficult to do anything with the prana or the mind directly, therefore, it is generally better to focus on the spaces or gaps between breath or thoughts. I do not recommend pranayama (direct control of the prana through breathing exercise) for people unless they live in a community or ashram that has a qualified teacher. It is very easy to imbalance the pranas with pranayama, easier, in fact, than balancing them. Pranayama should be done in a protected environment, with a teacher who can first give the right exercises according to your Ayurvedic constitution, and, second, watch your progress as the effects change your pranic balance. Finding a teacher qualified to fill these two requirements is rare in my experience.

If you like pranayama, and feel some karmic necessity to do it daily then, please, do it only for five to ten minutes per day. This will normally not be enough to imbalance the pranas in a lasting way. I have seen a number of people who have pranic imbalances from excessive meditation practices or inappropriate pranayama practices for their constitution.

A vegetarian diet is highly recommended if one practices meditation or pranayama. This is due to the opening of the nadis that results from the passage of an increased flow of prana in the meridians (nadis). The new level of prana passing releases toxins buried in the subtle levels of the body as well as the toxins lodged in the tissues. If these toxins are the accumulation of a meat diet, their release will cause problems for the practitioner on both a mental and physical level. The Ayurvedic **pancha**-karma purification methods should be done before starting, and again at three month intervals for one year if one starts pranayama from a meat-based diet. The mental rajas will then be better controlled and physical toxins purged.

The direct methods are also two. The first is to follow a thought back to its source; where does it come from? One does this by inquiring very intensely, "What is the source of this thought?" One can also intensely inquire into his or her ultimate nature by asking, "Who am I?" Both of these forms of inquiry are facilitated by negating anything that is not the source of the thought or the "I." This is a very old method given in the Upanishads. If this is intensely maintained, then one arrives at a thoughtless state. By staying in that state and, should any thought appear, inquiring to whom does this thought belong, then one comes close to knowing the substratum. There are, in fact, many states of subtle mind after the thoughts cease, but it is the place from which to begin. From here the "fourth" state can be experienced, that is neither waking, dreaming, nor deep sleep. The full identification with the substratum is called "beyond the fourth" because there is no one to call it the fifth. All personal identification has ceased.

The other direct method is to simply "be." This revolves around finding and recognizing the ever-present conscious sense that each of us has, our "I-ness." By holding onto, constantly being aware of, honoring this "is-ness" or "I-ness," the "fourth state" results. While this may look simple, it is considered to be the most difficult. The practice of exercises helps to develop the mental concentration needed for the utilization of the direct methods. Either of these two methods will result in identifying with Consciousness or the substratum.

The retraining of my mind (what I thought I was) to re-identify as Consciousness, the substratum, was instrumental in the recovery of my health. The lessening of action (rajas) or agitation in the mind, lessened fiery emotions (pitta), such as anger and self-negating (tamas) ones, such as anxiety (vata) and stress. The preoccupation with my agitated mental state and over-stressed emotions prevented me from giving attention to my physical body. By emphasizing the pure quality (satva) of intelligence, I was able to eliminate troublesome emotions and give my full attention to getting well. All of this generated the necessary energy to change external situations.

While other methods are also good, they should be considered as supplements to meditation, not as substitutes for it. Whatever one does helps. The other methods can help prepare one to work more directly on the question of re-identification with the substratum. The only exception to this is devotion or devotional prayer. However, my teacher (as well as others) points out that a devotional nature is very rare in the Western world due to our individualistic social conditioning. If devotion is your way, then love; it is enough because it is the substratum of the substratum.

14
Balancing the Humors

❂ *I have told you, Girija, the story of Rama that wipes out the
sins of the Kaliyuga and cleanses all the impurities of the mind,
the story that is a life-giving remedy for the disease of birth and
death, as is hymned by the Vedas and the learned.* ❂

Ultimately all treatments involve influencing prana in
one way or another. As we have seen throughout this book,
prana is the root of all manifestation, and is the basis of
the three humors. Through the therapies available in
Ayurveda one can maintain, recover, or create pranic harmony in the body. Additionally, with Ayurvedic life-style
therapies you can create pranic harmony in your personal
environment, and with Ayurvedic psychology you can increase mental peace.

In Ayurveda this pranic harmony is ordinarily perceived as the harmony of the three humors—vata, pitta,
and kapha. It can, however, be perceived directly as a balance of the five pranas. The primary concern here is the
fundamental knowledge that prana is the foundation of all
harmony in the body. This is clearly seen in the three humors by the instability of vata, the humor that relates
most directly to prana. Vata is considered to be the cause
of most diseases or imbalances in the body. It is also
known to empower the other two humors; they would be
motionless without vata. Therefore, Ayurvedic treatments
often involve vata and always work on the different forms
of prana as manifested through the three humors.

It should be noted that Ayurveda considers the use of
medicines (i.e., strong herbal and mineral preparations)
and surgery as last ditch efforts to recover health. Normally, people today regard taking medicines (in any form)
as a normal event if a disease or imbalance occurs. Just

look how easy it is to pop an aspirin when you have a headache from overwork. For Ayurveda this attitude is the real illness to be treated. All disease results from ignorance, which now translates as poor decisions regarding your life-style. Poor eating habits, poor mental habits, poor work environment and habits, a lack of spiritual and emotional nourishment—all these are the root causes of disease. Real Ayurvedic treatments must address these factors before herbs, foods, and other therapies, such as massage, are given. It is the basic failure to live in harmony with your nature—whatever your nature is—that results in the need to be treated in the first place. The continual use of medicines, whether herbal or synthetic, is a cop-out because the basic cause—ignorance—is not being confronted and changed. With the alleviation of ignorance harmony is achieved for the pranas and their manifestations as the three humors.

Ayurvedic therapies revolve around the use of: food, herbs, and life-style. Life-style includes very basic things, such as exercising, the appropriate times of the year and day for each activity, and other external factors. Foods and herbs as medicine form the basis for life-style therapies. By the same token, life-style therapies provide a solid foundation for food and herbal therapies. All three segments should be addressed for optimum results. Failure to address all three—food, herbs, and life-style—will tend to nullify the good results of the others practiced. I know a woman who religiously takes her herbs and eats very well; however, she fails to exercise regularly, and she smokes cigarettes. The smoking and lack of exercise virtually nullify the positive results of the correct diet and herbs. However, it does keep her body from deteriorating further, as would be the case if she stopped taking herbs and correct food daily.

Before treating—or self-treating—any disease or illness, several things need to be addressed. First, look at the overall condition of the person; i.e., weak or strong, young or old. Second, think about the amount of toxins that the person has in the body. Third, consider the strength of the digestion; can his or her body assimilate the herbs or foods? Fourth, think about the nature of the disease; i.e., internal cause or external cause, and the humors involved. Fifth, look at the mental disposition of the person; i.e., which guna or mental quality is predominant at this time, and is the person motivated enough to change bad habits? Is there enough discipline to takr the necessary herbs regularly? Self-love?

These questions must be considered before any kind of treatment is started. Failure to account for these factors will result in an ineffective treatment. To achieve effective treatment, these questions must be addressed. The practitioner's ability as a healer is directly concerned with his or her capacity to accurately perceive the patient's reality at the moment of treatment. By the same token, when we treat ourselves, we must be able to honestly address these same questions with sincerity.

Overall health is exactly what it implies—the general picture. This is the plot of the story. It gives as the outline of the story, where it began, and where it is going. It gives us the age, sex, and social condition of the patient. With this information, the practitioner can utilize a treatment that will fit the person. For example, I will not recommend an herb that is very costly if I know the person has little money. Nor will I treat the very old or very young the same as I would an adult. All these factors must be perceived and accounted for in any therapeutic approach.

Next, use tongue diagnosis to determine the current level of toxins. The general rule in Ayurveda is to detoxify before regenerating, otherwise the rejuvenating therapies will only strengthen the toxins, not the body. Therefore, detoxifying methods should be employed, provided the overall strength of the person will permit cleansing therapies. There are many different kinds of detoxification therapies, varying in strength and effectiveness. Obviously, if a person is weak or very ill, strong detox methods should not be used. In this case, the person should be given mild cleansing herbs, such as the triphala formula, that have a gentle action and, like triphala, also help regenerate the body.

The ability to digest food and herbs should be determined before prescribing any food or herbal therapies. Remember, Ayurveda states that it is the ability to assimilate what we ingest that determines the digestive strength. If the assimilation level is low, then herbs that improve or promote assimilation should be given. This is actually a question of agni; when agni is low it must be raised, when it is too high, it must be lowered. Attention must be given to make sure the preparation is digestible by the person. Vata persons will have difficulty digesting dry powders, so oily or wet vehicles must be used to transport the herbs. Pitta persons are normally okay with any kind of preparation provided their agni is strong; if not, add trikutu to the formula. Kapha people are best with warmer and dryer compounds that have hing or trikutu added to stimulate digestion.

The nature of the disease is important because, from an Ayurvedic point of view, it tells us which humors are involved, and the tissue level affected. It is not really necessary to know the name of the imbalance. To call a cold, a cold, is not therapeutically important. Neither is the Ayurvedic classification that it is an imbalance of kapha, generated by one of the three humors. These kinds of classifications can either be detrimental to the healing process of a person, or they can help in the healing process. If someone tells me that I have a tumor or high kapha, it can make a big difference in how I respond mentally to healing myself. By the same token, it may be a relief to know that I have a benign tumor and not cancer. Thus, classifying the humoral imbalance is, in my opinion, more helpful than attaching a name to the actual symptoms. Although, in any serious illness (like the example above) a qualified doctor should monitor all therapies and the health of the person. Perhaps it may be appropriate not to give any name whatsoever to disturbances. It is after all the nature of the mind to classify and create divisions where none exist.

The nature of the imbalance can be determined by the diagnostic methods described in chapter 9. It is important for the practitioner to know the root cause of the humoral imbalance, because all Ayurvedic therapies depend on knowing which humors are imbalanced. Balancing the humors or prana is the actual basis of Ayurvedic treatments. In the following section, we will look at how to balance each humor in a general setting. The most complete Ayurvedic approach to individual diseases and treatments can be found in *Ayurvedic Healing*.[1] I recommend this book as a household reference manual and to everyone interested in the actual Ayurvedic applications to specific diseases.

The last, but not least, factor to address before commencing any treatment is the mental state of the person. Failure to consider this aspect will nullify an otherwise correct treatment plan. An example of this situation happened in North India, where I lived for several years. Many of the Westerners who lived there, to hear the teachings of Sri Poonjaji, became sick with intestinal problems. This is a common problem in India, more people die there of amebic dysentery than any other disease. Many people went to see an old, reputedly good, Ayurvedic doctor with little or no results. Now this man was a fifth generation Ayurvedic doctor and was in his 80s. He obviously had plenty of experience and expertise; why then did his treatments fail?

A young American man cured 80 percent of these people of their intestinal problems by following Ayurvedic precepts, formulations, and herbal energetics. Why did a newcomer, with only several years of experience, cure so many people when a far more experienced doctor achieved a mere 1 or 2 percent? The answer lies in not addressing the mental and psychological position of the patients. The young man understood well the people he was treating; he was one of them. The other, more experienced doctor could not relate psychologically—he did not even try—to the people he was treating. This created a problem in both his

---

[1] Dr. David Frawley, *Ayurvedic Healing* (Salt Lake City, UT: Passage Press, 1989).

diagnosis and prescribed medication, which then resulted
in a failed treatment.

Ayurveda is a complete approach to healing. Failure
to account for the mental and psychological state of yourself (or your client) will tend to nullify the results from the
more physical treatments. In fact, this aspect is so important that a good doctor can heal people using any medical
system. It is his or her ability to heal, or harmonize, the
mental qualities of a person that actually results in stimulating the healing process, regardless of the medical system used.

Ultimately, it is the pranic field of the practitioner
that influences the healing process of the patient. Healing
cannot happen without this positive pranic exchange from
the healer to the healed. This is the secret of Yogic healing;
the Yogis' (or healers') pranic field calms and harmonizes
the pranic field of the person treated. The pranic field includes both the mental and physical state. The exchange
of prana results in a total healing. Without addressing the
mental and psychological aspects, Ayurveda is not
Ayurveda, it is just another symptomatic method of medical treatment.

In brief, the constitution of the person must be determined first. Then the overall physical health of the person
and the manifestations of the humoral imbalances is determined. The amount of toxins in the body and the digestive strength must also be addressed. Finally, the mental
and emotional state of the person is surmised. When all
this information is processed, the actual treatment can be
determined. Your ability to process this information will
determine your effectiveness in achieving results.

BALANCING VATA

Vata is directly related to the Apana Prana. The qualities
of vata are cold, dry, unstable, erratic, rough, and light.
The colors associated with vata are black or darkish colors. The pulse position is in the first position (closest to
the hand) and the back or root of the tongue shows the in-

ternal condition of vata. The site of vata is the large intestine, and it controls the organs of the lower half of the
body. Vata is responsible for all movement in the body
(muscular and nervous) and all excretions or wastes from
the body. Vata is directly related to the thinking process
and stress. External conditions of the skin and hair give
us indications of vata states (dryer, rough conditions indicate higher levels of vata). Sweet, sour and salty tastes decrease vata. By the same token, bitter, pungent, and astringent tastes increase vata. Vata is strongest in early
morning and in old age.

Any situation that involves the qualities or manifestations of vata indicates that vata is predominant in the
given circumstance. To the degree that vata is the force
that moves the other two humors, it is involved in every
illness. When it is the predominant force, it must be addressed directly. If it is not the predominant force, but present, then the predominant humor can be addressed in addition to vata. If vata is not involved directly, see the other
humors. Traditionally, Apana Prana is the most difficult of
the pranas to control, and thus explains the importance of
controlling vata.

Vata can be lowered by raising either pitta or kapha,
or both together; this results in "balance." The concept of
balance is relative to your constitution. For example, I am
predominantly pitta, with vata second, and I have little
kapha. To lower both pitta and vata (should vata be high) I
would increase the kapha humor. To lower only pitta I
could raise both vata and kapha. In another example, if
someone is a vata-kapha mix, then pitta can be raised to
harmonize the predominant two humors. Thus "balance"
does not mean three equal amounts of each humor, it
means *to return to your individual mix of the three
humors*, whatever that is for you.

For high vata conditions it is best to raise pitta and
kapha equally. If your vata condition leans toward the
pitta side (i.e., heat, inflammation, anger) then use more
kapha-type herbs and foods to lower vata. If your vata condition leans more toward kapha (i.e., wet, slow, dull,

lethargic), then use more pitta-type herbs and foods to lower vata.

Oil is good for all vata conditions, both externally and internally. Oils that have a heating action are best for controlling vata, like sesame or almond. To clear out internal toxins, castor oil is excellent for vata persons (take 1 tablespoon before bed). Oil massage is very important for controlling vata; massages should be given regularly with warming oils. Massage nourishes the skin, bones, and nerves.

To control vata, it is necessary to eliminate all cold, dry foods from the diet. These are mainly snack foods, such as cookies and chips, but drying foods (i.e., astringent) and breads also tend to aggravate vata. Cold drinks, especially "soft" drinks should be avoided. Complex foods or dishes should be avoided when vata is very high. Simple meals are easier to digest for vata people, and warm, hot, or cool drinks are best. Meat can be very grounding for vata; they are best able to handle meat if their digestion is strong enough. Meat soups are the best, as they are warming and nourishing.

Meditation, prayer, and quiet, nourishing times during the day are important for vata persons. Avoidance of stress, fear, and anxiety are important. Developing a regular life-style and habits is important also. Cultivating a kapha-like home—loving, solid, romantic, nourishing, emotionally enriching—is very helpful for controlling vata. Often low self-esteem or simply a lack of love is the cause of the very destructive vata habits. I have a friend who is VERY vata and she thrives on all the crazy things that imbalance vata. She is very social, helping many people with an infinite variety of things, has good self-esteem, yet has difficulty accepting love on more than a superficial level. The ability to love and receive love balances vata and all the five pranas.

BALANCING PITTA

Pitta is directly related to Samana Prana. The qualities of pitta are hot, oily, intense, light, and liquid. The colors associated with pitta are red, green, and yellow. Pitta is found in the second or middle pulse position, and is located in the middle area of the tongue. The site of pitta is the small intestine, and it controls the organs of digestion. Pitta controls the metabolism, body heat, and the transformation of matter and information. High or low body heat corresponds directly to pitta, as does the color of the complexion. A red or flushed complexion indicates higher amounts of pitta than pale or white complexions. Sweet, bitter, and astringent tastes lower pitta, while sour, salty, and pungent tastes increase pitta. Pitta is strongest in the middle of the day and in midlife.

Strong, hot emotions indicate that pitta is too high and needs to be lowered. Burning sensations in the body, or inflamed conditions, show excess amounts of pitta. Low body heat, lethargy, and dullness of mind indicate a lack of pitta. Meditation and prayer help to lower the fiery emotions associated with pitta. A stable, loving home environment also helps to keep pitta from overheating. A satvic lifestyle and diet are very useful to control pitta. The satvic way of living is the most important for pitta-type people as they are the ones who are most likely to dominate, control, and aggress other people. Eating and living a satvic life is an excellent way to lower high pitta emotions.

Pitta can be lowered by raising kapha. In general, a kapha-like diet and life-style are very beneficial for pitta people who have good digestion. If an excess of oily hot matter is predominant anywhere in the body, then vata-type foods and herbs can also be used in conjunction with kapha-type substances. Cold, bitter (vata) herbs are excellent for lowering pitta and detoxifying the blood and pitta organs—liver, spleen, pancreas, and small intestine. Cooling foods and drinks should be taken to lower pitta when it is aggravated. Spices and hot, spicy foods should be avoided when pitta is high. And the best new^{T}s is (for me) that ice cream is fine for pitta people (in moderation)!

Pitta-type digestive problems should also address vata, as the two are generally involved, especially in long-term or ignored cases of indigestion. Usually, pitta will move down, or vata will move up, to aggravate the other humor. Because pitta controls the mixing of all digestive bile with food, vata is directly affected by pitta's malfunction. Diarrhea is both a pitta and vata problem, as is constipation.

Malabsorption is a pitta problem relating directly to low agni, thus agni must be increased with herbs like the trikutu formula, hing, cumin, anise, and fennel. These are all excellent to increase agni. Even if pitta is not your primary problem, indentations on the tongue's edge show the malabsorption of nutrients, and this can happen to any constitution. Steps must be taken to eat very simply— whole grains and steamed vegetables, in addition to the correct spices. In this way, agni can be slowly increased and the nutrient absorption increased. Lactobacillus acidophilus supplements are also useful in this situation. The triphala formula, ghee, and miso can also play important roles in increasing agni.

In general, whatever pitta people do for their mental and emotional states is the best therapy. Massage with cooling oils (olive, coconut) is good once or twice a week, as it helps to cool down the body and release toxins that can manifest as strong emotions. Sports or other physical activities are very important to help pitta people positively express their abundance of energy.

BALANCING KAPHA

Kapha is directly related to the Vyana Prana. The qualities of kapha are cold, oily, heavy, dense, stable, and smooth. The colors associated with kapha are white and pale tones. Kapha corresponds to the third pulse position (closest to the shoulder) and is found on the front part of the tongue. Kapha is located in the stomach and corresponds to the organs in the upper half of the body. Kapha provides the quality of cohesion to the body and forms the base or foundation for the other two humors. Smooth conditions of the skin indicate kapha along with white or pale colors. Pungent, bitter, and astringent tastes decrease kapha, while sweet, sour, and salty tastes increase kapha. Kapha is strongest in mid-morning and childhood.

Excessive sleep, lethargy, and a dull mind indicate that the kapha humor is overabundant and needs to be lowered. Obesity or excess fat accumulation also shows an excess of kapha, and often a malfunction of pitta. As pitta controls the metabolism and the digestion, an excess of kapha can "put out the fire" so to speak. Thus, raising pitta is the basis of treating most kapha imbalances. Heating herbs and foods can provide the means needed to raise pitta.

Detoxifying plays a very important role in treating kapha people. The malfunctioning, or substandard functioning, of the metabolism allows toxins to accumulate in the tissues of the body. For this to happen the digestive tract and blood must also be involved. Thus the whole body is polluted with an abnormal level of toxic matter. This is the cause of many kapha-type diseases, such as obesity and diabetes. Even just a lack of energy can be the sign of toxic accumulation in the body. Kapha people do not have to be overweight, slow, or diabetic to have high or aggravated kapha. Lethargy, excessive sleep, low energy, depression, and a lack of motivation are all signs of high kapha. Information on lowering weight is given in chapter 10 for those interested.

It is usually helpful for kapha people to work with others in groups or classes, as this is more emotionally nourishing, and also allows the group energy to keep the person motivated and active. Quality relationships are very important for kapha people; superficial relationships are depressing and draining for sentimental and romantic kapha types. Outside activities and soft forms of exercises help to control kapha. Family activities are a good way to get kapha people out of their houses and into the fresh air.

Foods should be very light and warm to lower kapha. Building therapies or herbs should only be taken after detoxifying the whole body. Kapha people must not try to starve themselves in order to lose weight or stay thin. This has many negative repercussions psychologically. It is best for kapha people to use gradual dietary regimes that work slowly but surely. The Triphala Guggulu formula is very valuable for the kapha problems of cholesterol and metabolism.

Kapha people must be patient and persistent in all the life-style plans and regimens. They will achieve results more slowly, but they will achieve results with patience and persistence. Generally the first month or two can be spent detoxifying and the following months can be used to balance the metabolism. Throughout this period efforts should be taken to increase the digestive ability by using the Trikutu formula or other digestive spices, such as ginger, cumin, fennel, turmeric, peppers, and chilies, when appropriate.

BALANCING MIXED CONSTITUTIONS

People of mixed constitutions can be treated by combining the qualities of the two predominant humors and then using the remaining one to lower the two elevated ones. For example, a vata-kapha person can use pitta therapies to lower the constitution and so gain harmony. A vata-pitta person can use kapha therapies to bring harmony, while the pitta-kapha person will use vata-type therapies for balance, although this approach must be done with care as vata is unstable.

Keep in mind that it is always the positive qualities of every humor that are used to balance other humors. Strong heat therapies—pitta—can be therapeutic to both kapha and vata constitutions, but they should only be administered by a qualified Ayurvedic practitioner. So too for any extreme therapies that you may be tempted to use. This is especially important for a person with a mixed constitution. The mixed type often achieves slower results and may want to go faster than is possible for their nature, especially when kapha is one of the main humors.

Diets for mixed types can be chosen according to season and the strongest digestive problem. This means that if you have a constipation problem you would treat yourself with an anti-vata diet (vata-kapha or vata-pitta). If vata is not one of your two mixes (kapha-pitta), then you would probably have a low pitta problem, thus a pro-pitta (or anti-kapha) diet would benefit you. These are general guidelines; if you have doubt, then it is advised that you consult an Ayurvedic practitioner.

What I do in my practice is to suggest one regimen for a diet and one for life-style. For example, a vata-kapha person may be overweight, but this person has a quick mind that moves all over the place, making it difficult to follow a diet or plan to lose wieght. In this case I suggest that the person follow an anti-vata (what lowers vata) life-style and an anti-kapha diet. One benefits the body, the other benefits the mind *and* body. In practical applications, I find this method to be simple and effective. Experience shows that life-style has an overall balancing effect, whereas diet has a more immediate relationship to the body. If the tongue has vata cracks on it, especially deep ones, then an anti-vata life-style *must* be followed, regardless of the natal constitution, as it indicates a chronic imbalance of vata.

DIET INFORMATION

Here are some brief guidelines on the right foods for lowering each humor. As the majority of us experience aggravated humors, I have simplified the dietary recommendations as much as possible by only giving the foods that LOWER an aggravated humor. This will tend to increase the opposite humor or humors, resulting in harmony. Bear in mind that this is a simplistic approach compared to the extremely precise information available for Ayurvedic regimens. In general, fresh natural foods are the best to eat. Avoid processed foods of any kind, and avoid white sugar. Meat may be taken according to your constitution. If you have a special occasion, you may eat anything you want and go back to your balancing diet the next day, just note any effects that may occur to bring validation to your new diet. Most people start to feel so much better after a few weeks of eating like this that no confirmation is necessary!

I usually suggest that people begin by using these dietary guidelines 70 to 80 percent of the time. As they become more accustomed to eating and choosing different foods they can slowly adapt to following it 99.9 percent (after all there's still Christmas!).

Antitoxic diet

An antitoxic diet is one that should be used if your tongue is coated with a film, or if you exhibit other signs of toxic accumulation in the body. This diet consists of light whole grains, steamed veggies, and pure water. Fruit can be taken in between meals, or alone for breakfast. In this diet fruit cannot be eaten with other foods. Foods should not be mixed very much; in other words, do not steam five kinds of veggies together at the same time, have three different grains, salad, fruit juice, and dessert. While this is fine for a normal diet, it has nothing to do with detoxifying the body. Keep the meals simple and nourishing. All dairy products should be avoided along with meat and fish. Chicken soup may be taken if you feel you will die without meat. Foods must be fresh and prepared by you or your family. Use this diet for one or two weeks.

Basmati rice, barley, and quinoa are very good grains to use. Veggies can be chosen from the lists below according to your constitution. Water is the best thing to drink to purify the body, however, herbal teas can be taken also. Warming teas are good for vata and kapha, and cooling teas are good for pitta. Flower teas are usually cooling, aromatic leaves are often heating, roots can be either. Good references for the best teas are found in *The Yoga of Herbs* and *The Ayurvedic Cookbook*.[2] Complete food lists can be found in books written by the students of Dr. Vasant Lad or directly from his Ayurvedic Institute in New Mexico.

---

[2]Dr. David Frawley & Dr. Vasant Lad, *Yoga of Herbs* (Twin Lakes, WI: Lotus Press, 1986); and Amadea Morningstar, *The Ayurvedic Cookbook* (Twin Lakes, WI: Lotus Press, 1990).

Lower Vata Diet

To lower vata use the following foods:

Sweet fruits
Apricots
Avocados
Bananas
Berries
Citrus (not sour)
Melons
Peaches

Cooked veggies
Asparagus
Carrots
Cucumber
Green beans
Leeks
Olives
Onions
Sweet potatoes
Pumpkins
Squash

Grains
Oats

All kinds of rice
Wheat

Meats/Eggs
Chicken
Turkey
Duck
Fish
Seafood
Eggs

Beans
Go easy on the beans
Aduki
Mung (or moong)
Lentils
Soy milk
Tofu (cooked)

All nuts are okay
All dairy is okay

All oils are okay

Lower Pitta Diet

To lower pitta use the following foods:

Sweet fruits
Apples
Avocados
Berries
Dates
Figs
Grapes

Melons
Pears
Plums

Vegetables
Sweet and bitter veggies
Artichokes

Asparagus
Broccoli
Brussel sprouts
Cabbage
Corn
Cauliflower
Leafy greens
Lettuce
Mushrooms
Potatoes
Squash

Beans
Aduki beans
Black beans
Garbanzos
Kidney beans
Lima
Mung
Pinto
Soybeans and soy products
Tofu
Coconut

Grains
Barley
Cooked oats
Basmatirice
White rice
Wheat

Dairy
Butter
Cottage cheese
Soft cheeses
Ghee
Mllk
Ice cream!

Meat/Eggs
Chicken
Turkey
Rabbit
Eggs

Oils
Coconut oil
Olive oil
Sunflower oil
Soy oil

Lower Kapha Diet

To lower kapha use the following foods:

Bitter and astringent
fruits
Apricots
Berries
Cherries
Cranberries
Peaches
Pears
Persimmons

Pomegranates
Prunes
Raisins

Vegetables
Pungent and bitter veggies
Asparagus
Beets
Broccoli

Cabbage
Carrots
Cauliflower
Corn
Eggplant
Garlic
Leafy greens
Leeks
Mushrooms
Onions
Peas
Peppers
Spinach
Sprouts
Turnips

Grains
Barley
Buckwheat
Corn
Quinoa
Rye

Meat/Eggs
Chicken
Turkey
Boiled eggs

Beans
Aduki beans
Lima beans
Navy beans
Pinto beans
Split peas
White beans

No nuts

No dairy

Oils
Almond oil
Corn oil
Sunflower oil

In general, you should use the diet that lowers your constitutional humor; however, in cases of imbalance or aggravation anyone can use any of the above diets to control an imbalance. If any doubt persists, consult an Ayurvedic practitioner.

RAM! RAM! RAM!
MAY PEACE BE WITH ALL BEINGS!
OM! OM! OM!

Appendix
Latin, Indian and English Herbal Correspondences

HERBS LISTED ALPHABETICALLY BY LATIN NAMES

LATIN NAME	INDIAN NAME	ENGLISH NAME
Asafoetida	Hing	Asatoetida
Asparagus adescendens	Safed Mushali	White Asparagus
Asparagus racemosus	Shatavri	Asparagus
Asphaltum	Shilajit	Mineral Pitch
Azadiracta Indica	Neem	Neem
Bambusa arundinacia	Vamsha Rochana	Bamboo Manna
Berberis arista	Daru Haldi	Wood Turmeric
Boerhaavia diffusa	Punarnava	Hog weed
Caryophyllus aromaticus	Lavanga	Clove
Cinnamomum zeylanicum	Dalchini	Cinnamon
Cinnamomum iners	Tejpatra	Tamala
Convolvoios pluricaulis	Shankpushpi	Shankpushpi
Commiphora mukul	Guggulu	Guggulu
Crocus sativus	Kesar	Saffron
Cumimum cyminum	Safed Jerra	White Cumin
Curcuma longa	Haldi	Turmeric
Cyperus rotundus	Musta	Nut Grass
Eclipta alba	Bhringraj	Eclipta
Eliataria cardamomum	Elacihi	Cardamom
Emblica officinalis	Amalaki	Indian Gooseberry
Embelia ribes	Vidanga	Embelia
Foeniculum vulgare	Bari Saunf	Fennel
Glycyrrhiza giabra	Mulethi	Licorice

HERBS LISTED ALPHABETICALLY BY LATIN NAMES (cont.)

LATIN NAME	INDIAN NAME	ENGLISH NAME
Hemidesmus indicus..........	Anantmool..........	Indian Sarsaparilla
Hydrocotyle asiatica...........	Brahmi................	Gotu Kola
Mucuna pruriens..................	Kaunch................	Cowhage
Myristica fragrans...............	Jaiphal................	Nutmeg
Nardostachys jatamanal.....	Jatamansi...........	Spikenard
Nelumbo nucifera...............	Kamal Bees........	Lotus Seeds
Nigelia sativa.......................	Kali Jerra............	Black Cumin
Ocimum sanctum.................	Tulsi....................	Holy Basil
Picrorrhiza kurroa...............	Kutki...................	Picrorrhiza
Piper longum.......................	Pippli..................	Long Pepper
Piper nigrum........................	Kalimirch............	Black Pepper
Plumbago zeylanica............	Chitrak................	Ceylon Leadwort
Polygonatum officinale.......	Meda...................	Solomon Seal
Pterocarpus santalinus.......	Rakta Chandana.	Red Sandalwood
Rubia cordifolia...................	Manjishta............	Indian Madder
Santalum alba......................	Chandana...........	Sandalwood
Sida cordifolia.....................	Bala....................	Country Mallow
Swertia chirata....................	Chiraita...............	Indian Gentian
Terminalia belerica..............	Bibhitaki.............	Beleric myrobalan
Terminalla chebula..............	Heritaki...............	Chebulic myrobalan
Tinispora cordifolia..............	Guduchi..............	Amrita
Tribulis terrestris.................	Gokshura...........	Caltrops
Valeriana wallichi.................	Thagara..............	Indian Valerian
Withania somnifera..............	Ashwagandha.....	Winter Cherry
Zingiber officinale...............	Sunthi.................	Ginger

HERBS LISTED ALPHABETICALLY BY INDIAN NAMES

LATIN NAME	INDIAN NAME	ENGLISH NAME
Emblica officinalis................	Amalaki............	Indian Gooseberry
Hemidesmus indicus.............	Anantmool........	Indian Sarsaparilla
Withania somnifera...............	Ashwagandha....	Winter Cherry
Foeniculum vulgare..............	Bari Saunf.........	Fennel
Sida cordifolia.....................	Bala..................	Country Mallow
Eclipta alba........................	Bhringraj...........	Eclipta
Terminalia belerica..............	Bibhitaki............	Beleric myrobalan
Hydrocotype asiatica............	Brahmi...............	Gotu Kola
Plumbago zeylanica..............	Chitrak...............	Ceylon Leadwort
Santalum alba.....................	Chandana..........	Sandalwood
Swertia chirata....................	Chiraita.............	Indian Gentian
Berberis arista.....................	Daru Haldi.........	Wood Turmeric
Cinnamomum zeylanicum......	Dalchini.............	Cinnamon
Ellataria cardamomum..........	Elacihi...............	Cardamom
Tribulis terrestris..................	Gokshura..........	Caltrops
Commiphora mukul...............	Guggulu............	Guggulu
Tinispora cordifolia..............	Guduchi............	Amrita
Curcuma longa....................	Haldi.................	Turmeric
Terminalia chebula...............	Haritaki.............	Chebulic myrobalan
Asafoetida..........................	Hing..................	Asafoetida
Myristica fragrans................	Jaiphal..............	Nutmeg
Nardostachys jatamansi........	Jatamansi..........	Spikenard
Nelumbo nucifera.................	Kamal Bees.......	Lotus Seeds
Nigelia sativa......................	Kali Jerra...........	Black Cumin
Piper nigrum.......................	Kalimirch...........	Black Pepper
Mucuna pruriens..................	Kaunch.............	Cowhage
Crocus sativus....................	Kesar................	Saffron
Picrorrhiza kurroa................	Kutki.................	Picrorrhiza
Caryophyllus aromaticus........	Lavanga...........	Clove
Rubia cordifolia...................	Manjishta...........	Indian Madder
Polygonatum officinale..........	Meda.................	Solomon Seal
Cyperus rotundus................	Musta................	Nut Grass
Glycyrrhiza glabra................	Mulethi..............	Licorice
Azadiracta indica.................	Neem................	Neem
Piper longum......................	Pippli................	Long Pepper

HERBS LISTED ALPHABETICALLY BY INDIAN NAMES (cont.)

LATIN NAME	INDIAN NAME	ENGLISH NAME
Boerhaavia diffusa...............	**Punarnava**...........	Hog weed
Pterocarpus santalinus........	**Rakta Chandana**...	Red Sandalwood
Asparagus adescendens.....	**Safed Mushali**.......	White Asparagus
Cumimum cyminum............	**Safed Jerra**...........	White Cumin
Asparagus racemosus........	**Shatavri**.................	Asparagus
Asphaltum......................	**Shilajit**...................	Mineral Pitch
Convolvolos pluricaulis........	**Shankpushpi**........	Shankpushpi
Zingiber officinale...............	**Sunthi**...................	Ginger
Cinnamomum iners............	**Tejpatra**................	Tamala
Valeriana wallichi................	**Thagara**................	Indian Valerian
Ocimum sanctum................	**Tulsi**.....................	Holy Basil
Bambusa arundinacia.........	**Vamsha Rochana.**	Bamboo Manna
Embelia ribes...................	**Vidanga**...............	Embelia

HERBS LISTED ALPHABETICALLY BY ENGLISH NAMES

LATIN NAME	INDIAN NAME	ENGLISH NAME
Tinispora cordifolia.............	Guduchi..............	Amrita
Asafoetida..........................	Hing.....................	Asafoetida
Asparagus racemosus.........	Shatavri...............	Asparagus
Bambusa arundinacia..........	Vamsha Rochana..	Bamboo Manna
Terminalia belerica.............	Bibhitaki...............	Beleric myrobalan
Nigelia sativa.....................	Kali Jerra..............	Black Cumin
Piper nigrum.......................	Kalimirch..............	Black Pepper
Ellataria cardamomum........	Elacihi..................	Cardamom
Tribulis terrestris.................	Gokshura..............	Caltrops
Plumbago zeylanica............	Chitrak..................	Ceylon Leadwort
Terminalia chebula..............	Haritaki.................	Chebulic myrobalan
Cinnamomum zeylanicum...	Dalchini.................	Cinnamon
Caryophyllus aromaticus.....	Lavanga................	Clove
Sida cordifolia....................	Bala......................	Country Mallow
Mucuna pruriens..................	Kaunch.................	Cowhage
Eclipta alba........................	Bhringraj..............	Eclipta
Embelia ribes......................	Vidanga................	Embelia
Foeniculum vulgare.............	Bari Saunf.............	Fennel
Zingiber officinale...............	Sunthi...................	Ginger
Hydrocotyle asiatica............	Brahmi..................	Gotu Kola
Commiphora mukul..............	Guggulu................	Guggulu
Boerhaavia diffusa..............	Punarnava.............	Hog weed
Ocimum sanctum.................	Tulsi.....................	Holy Basil
Swertia chirata...................	Chiraita................	Indian Gentian
Emblica officinalis...............	Amalaki.................	Indian Gooseberry
Rubia cordifolia...................	Manjishta..............	Indian Madder
Hemidesmus indicus............	Anantmool.............	Indian Sarsaparilla
Valeriana wallichi................	Thagara................	Indian Valerian
Glycyrrhiza glabra................	Mulethi.................	Licorice
Nelumbo nucifera................	Kamal Bees..........	Lotus Seeds
Piper longum......................	Pippli....................	Long Pepper
Asphaltum..........................	Shilajit..................	Mineral Pitch
Azadiracta indica.................	Neem....................	Neem

HERBS LISTED ALPHABETICALLY BY ENGLISH NAMES (cont.)

LATIN NAME	INDIAN NAME	ENGLISH NAME
Cyperus rotundus..................	Musta...................	Nut Grass
Myristica fragrans..................	Jaiphal................	Nutmeg
Picrorrhiza kurroa..................	Kutki...................	Picrorrhiza
Pterocarpus santalinus..........	Rakta Chandana.	Red Sandalwood
Crocus sativus......................	Kesar...................	Saffron
Santalum alba......................	Chandana............	Sandalwood
Convolvolos pluricaulis.........	Shankpushpi.......	Shankpushpi
Polygonatum officinale..........	Meda...................	Solomon Seal
Nardostachys jatamansi........	Jatamansi...........	Spikenard
Cinnamomum iners................	Tejpatra..............	Tamala
Curcuma longa.....................	Haldi...................	Turmeric
Asparagus adescendens.......	Safed Mushali.....	White Asparagus
Cumimum cyminum...............	Safed Jerra.........	White Cumin
Withania somnifera...............	Ashwagandha.....	Winter Cherry
Berberis arista.....................	Daru Haldi..........	Wood Turmeric

Glossary

Agni: First of three cosmic principles; god of fire; digestive fire.

Agnivasa: The sage who first compiled the text now known as the Caraka Samhita.

Allopathy: Western medicine, modern medicine.

Apana prana: One of the five pranas; the prana that controls all evacuation, called the downward breath; resides in the lower abdomen.

Aphrodisiac: Any substance that promotes health to the reproductive organs.

Ashram: Place devoted to spiritual development.

Atma: Consciousness, or God in an individualized sense.

Atreya: The teacher of Agnivasa and source of the Caraka Samhita.

Ayurveda: The oldest medical system in the world. A holistic approach developed by the same sages who formed the systems of yoga. The part of the Vedas dealing with the health of the body; the science of life.

Brahma: Consciousness, or God in an absolute sense; one of the three aspects of God, the creator or creative aspect; the founder of Ayurveda.

Brahmin: The learned class of people in Vedic society; priests.

Brahmacharya: Abidance in Brahma or God.

Caraka Samhita: The oldest surviving text of Ayurveda.

Chi: Chinese word for Prana.

Chit: Consciousness.

Consciousness: As used in this book, the substratum or source of all manifestation; God.

Constitution: An individual's unique mix of the three humors.

Dosha: Sanskrit for humor; lit., "that which will imbalance."

Energetic Impressions: In Sanskrit there are two kinds: Vasanas and Samskaras; these are latent, unconscious, or stored impressions and current mental impressions; these impressions are stored in the subtle body; Yoga says that these impressions are what cause us to incarnate in another life, unless they are allowed to surface to consciousness; these impressions along with prana create what we call mind.

Inquiry: Method to find out where thoughts, prana arise from; question: "Who am I?"; see books of Ramana Maharishi and H. W. L. Poonjaji.

Five elements: The five states of material existence: mass, liquidity, transformation, movement, and the field in which they function; also called: earth, water, fire, air, and ether.

Five states of matter: Commonly called the Five Elements.

Ghee: Butter that has gone through a process of cooking to render it free from deterioration; used for cooking and as a vehicle for herbal medicines.

Guna: Quality, attribute of intelligence; there are three gunas: satva, rajas, and tamas; therapeutically it is the quality of an herb or substance, i.e., oily, slimy, dry, etc.

Guru: Lit. "dispeller of ignorance"; one who knows the substratum or source of creation; teacher; heavy.

Humor: A unique concept to describe the functions of the body; the forces which control the five elements together in the body; there are three humors: vata (wind), pitta (fire), and kapha (water).

Immunomodulator: A substance that works indirectly to help the immune system; usually keeps on affecting the body after use is discontinued, therefore better for long- term rejuvenation.

Immunostimulant: A substance that works directly on the immune system; usually has effect only as long as you take the substance, therefore better for immediate needs—colds, etc.

Kapha: One of the three humors; controls the water and earth elements.

Karma: Action; the cosmic law of for every action there is a reaction; there is no such thing as "bad or good" karma; therapeutically it is the general action of an herb or substance in the body.

Ki: Japanese word for prana.

Kundalini: The primordial prana that rests dormant in the body unless activated by special practices. NOTE: these practices are dangerous unless one is supervised by a qualified teacher.

Latent impression: See Energetic impressions.

Life Force: Another name of prana.

Marma: The acupressure and acupuncture points of Ayurveda.

Maya: The illusion that everyone exists as separate from God.

Meridians: The channels of prana in the body; called nadis in yoga.

Mind: Thoughts moving through consciousness, giving the illusion of continuity; the combination of prana and vasanas.

Nadi: See Meridian.

No-Mind: Nonmovement of thought; complete awareness; not to be confused with the Absolute, the individual may still exist at this point, it may take many times of being emerged in no-mind before the individual dissolves into pure consciousness.

Ojas: The essence of food; the basis of the immune system; we are born with eight drops of ojas in the heart center, if this is reduced, death results; there is a secondary ojas which is the result of all the tissue elements; it can vary in quantity, however, when it is reduced, sickness results (ref.: Caraka Samhita, vol. I, p. 594).

Parabdha: The karma or action that is residual; the karmas associated with the body/mind manifestation, in other words, as long as you have a body the Parabdha karma continues.

Pitta: One of the three humors; controls the fire and water elements.

Prabhava: The specific action of an herb or substance.

Prakriti: The dynamic energy of consciousness; natal constitution; nature.

Prana: *Pra* = before, *ana* = breath; the vital force; Qi, Ki, Chi; it arises from substratum of pure consciousness with intelligence (agni) and love (soma), together they create the individualized consciousness. There are five major pranas in the human body—prana, apana, samana, udana and vyana; they arise from the Cosmic Prana, chief of the five pranas in the body; also called the outward going breath, it resides in the head and the heart.

Pranayama: A method of breath control used to regulate the mind and prana, thereby physical and mental health. Should only be practiced with a qualified teacher.

Pranic healing: A therapeutic method that harmonizes the pranas directly.

Purusha: The inert aspect of consciousness; the void.

Qi: Another name for prana.

Rajas: One of the three gunas; action, movement, bright, energy, aggression, aggravated mind, achievement, and strong emotions.

Rama: The disciple of Vasishta and the student that receives the teaching in the Yoga Vasistha; avatar; one of the manifestations of Vishnu, the force of preservation in the universe; the hero of the epic poem Ramayana; pure consciousness embodied.

Ramayana: The story of Rama restoring harmony to the world.

Rasa: The first action of an herb or substance in the body; lit., "taste."

Samana prana: One of the five pranas in the body; called the equalizing prana, it resides in the navel region.

Samsara: The concept that we are separate from God; suffering; illusion.

Samskaras: Innate energetic impressions, see Energetic impressions.

Satva: One of the three gunas; purity, peace, calm, beauty, happiness, quiet obedient mind, and stable emotions.

Satvic diet: A diet that promotes satva; very mild nourishing foods, such as milk, basmati rice, mung beans, and fruits.

Self: Another name of God, or Consciousness.

Shakti: Cosmic prana.

Shiva: God as pure Consciousness; one of the three aspects of God, the destroyer.

Soma: Nectar; the most subtle essence of ojas and kapha; the God Soma signifies love, unity.

Substratum: Equal to the Absolute, Consciousness, God, Love, Brahman, Atman, Self, or Source.

Tamas: One of the three gunas; inertia, dull, depressed, void, stupid, lazy, despair, and self-destructive emotions.

Tantra: A path that totally accepts all aspects of the physical world, believing that all things lead to the divine; worship of the divine mother; often confused as being limited to sex.

Taste: The beginning of the therapeutic actions of any substance on the body.

Trikutu: A famous Ayurvedic formula that stimulates digestion and agni; very good for kapha and vata.

Triphala: A famous Ayurvedic formula for rejuvenating the body, promoting digestion, and harmonizing all the digestive organs.

Udana prana: One of the five pranas in the body; called the upward moving breath, it is seated in the throat; kundalini yoga cultivates this prana, as do all psychic powers.

Vakruti: The constitution of the moment.

Vasanas: Latent energetic impression, see Energetic impressions.

Vasishta: The most prominent sage in the Vedas; one of the seven immortal seers; the teacher in the Yoga Vasishta of Rama.

Vata: One of the three humors; controls the wind (air) and ether elements.

Vayu: The God of the Wind; another name for vata; another name for prana.

Vedas: Literally it means knowledge, but used here to mean the Book of Knowledge, the oldest book in the world; there are four Vedas.

Vipaka: The long-term effect of an herb or substance.

Virya: The potency (hot or cold) of an herb or substance.

Vishnu: God as pure love; the aspect of God that protects and preserves the world; He has seven main manifestations, of which Rama and Krishna are the two most famous.

Vyana prana: One of the five pranas in the body; called the equalizing breath, it unifies all the other pranas and the body; it is diffused throughout the body.

Yoga: Union; that which leads one back to the original Source; generally understood to mean a path or a practice leading to the Divine.

Bibliography

BOOKS ON HEALING

Athavale, Dr. V. B. *Pulse.* Bombay, India: Pediatric Clinics of India, 1976.

Beinfield, Harriet. *Between Heaven and Earth: A Guide to Chinese Medicine.* New York: Ballantine Books, 1991.

Chia, Mantak and Michael Winn. *Taoist Secrets of Love: Cultivating Male Sexual Energy.* Santa Fe: Aurora Press, 1984.

Chia, Mantak and Maneewan. *Healing Love through the Tao: Cultivating Female Sexual Energy.* Jim Thorpe, PA: Healing Tao Books, 1986.

Clifford, Dr. Terry. *Tibetan Buddhist Medicine and Psychiatry.* York Beach, ME: Samuel, Weiser, 1984.

Dash, Dr. Bhagwan. *Ayurvedic Cures for Common Diseases.* Delhi, India: Hind Pocket Books, 1993, 4th ed.

————.*Materia Medica of Ayurveda.* New Delhi, India: B. Jain Publishers, 1991.

Dash, Dr. Bhagwan, and Dr. R. K. Sharma. *Caraka Samhita.* 3 vols. Varanasi, India: Chowkamba Series Office, 1992.

Devaraj, Dr. T. L. *Speaking of: Ayurvedic Remedies for Common Diseases.* New Delhi, India: Sterling Publishers, 1985.

Frawley, Dr. David. *Ayurveda and the Mind.* Twin Lakes, WI: Lotus Press, 1997.

————. *Ayurvedic Healing: A Comprehensive Guide.* Salt Lake City, UT: Passage Press, 1989.

————. *From the River of Heaven.* Salt Lake City, UT: Passage Press, 1990.

————. *Gods, Sages and Kings.* Salt Lake City, UT: Passage Press, 1991.

————. *Tantric Yoga and the Wisdom Goddesses.* Salt Lake City, UT: Passage Press, 1994.

Frawley, Dr. David, and Dr. Vasant Lad. *The Yoga of Herbs.* Twin Lakes, WI: Lotus Press, 1986.

Gambhirananda, Swami, trans. *Eight Upanishads.* Vols. I and II. Calcutta, India: Advaita Ashrama, 1991, 2nd ed.

Heyn, Birgit. *Ayurvedic Medicine: The Gentle Strength of Indian Healing.* New Delhi, India: Indus HarperCollins India, 1992.

Joshi, Dr. Sunil V. *Ayurveda and Panchakarma.* Twin Lakes, WI: Lotus Press, 1996.

Kaptchuk, Dr. Ted J. *The Web That Has No Weaver.* Chicago: Congdon & Weed, 1983.

Lad, Dr. Vasant. *Ayurveda: The Science of Self-Healing.* Twin Lakes, WI: Lotus Press, 1984.

———. *Secrets of the Pulse.* Albuqerque, NM: The Ayurvedic Institute, 1996.

Lad, Dr. Vasant, and Usha Lad. *Ayurvedic Cooking for Self-Healing.* Twin Lakes, WI: Lotus Press, 1994.

Morningstar, Amadea. *The Ayurvedic Cookbook.* Twin Lakes, WI: Lotus Press, 1990.

———. *Ayurvedic Cooking for Westerners.* Twin Lakes, WI: Lotus Press, 1994.

Ranade, Dr. Subhash. *Natural Healing through Ayurveda.* Salt Lake City, UT: Passage Press, 1993.

Ros, Dr. Frank. *The Lost Secrets of Ayurvedic Acupuncture.* Twin Lakes, WI: Lotus Press, 1994.

Sachs, Melanie. *Ayurvedic Beauty Care.* Twin Lakes, WI: Lotus Press, 1994.

Sharma, Dr. Priya Vrat. *Sodasangahrdayam: Essentials of Ayurveda.* Delhi, India: Motilal Banarsidass, 1993.

Sivarajan, V. V. *Ayurvedic Drugs and their Plant Sources.* New Delhi, India: Oxford Publishing, 1994.

Svoboda, Dr. Robert. *Prakruti: Your Ayurvedic Constitution.* Albuquerque, NM: Geocom, 1989.

———. *Ayurveda: Life, Health and Longevity.* New Delhi, India: Penguin Books India, 1993.

Tierra, Michael. *Planetary Herbology.* Twin Lakes, WI: Lotus Press, 1988.

———. *The Way of Herbs.* New York: Pocket Books, 1980

SPIRITUAL VISIONS

Nisargadatta, Maharaj. *I Am That.* Bombay, India: Chetana, 1991.

———. *Prior to Consciousness.* Durham, NC: Acorn Press, 1985.

————. *Seeds of Consciousness.* Durham, NC: Acorn Press, 1990.

————. *Consciousness and the Absolute.* Durham, NC: Acorn Press, 1994.

Poonja, Sri H. W. L., *The Truth Is.* Huntington Beach, CA: Yudhishtara, 1995.

————. *Wake Up And Roar,* vols. I & II. Kula, Maui, Hawaii: Pacific Center Pub., 1992.

————. *Papaji.* David Godman, ed. Boulder, CO: Avadhuta Foundation, 1993.

Ramana Maharishi. *Be As You Are.* David Godman, ed. New Delhi, India: Penguin Books India, 1992.

————. *Talks with Sri Ramana Maharishi.* Swami Ramanananda, trans. Tiruvannamalai, India: Sri Ramanasramam, 1984.

Ramanananda, Swami, trans. *Advaita Bodha Deepika.* Tiruvannamalai, India: Sri Ramanasramam, 1990.

————. trans. *Tripura Rahasya.* Tiruvannamalai, India: Sri Ramanasramam, 1989.

Tulasidasa's Shriramacharitamanasa. R. C. Prasad, trans, and ed. Delhi, India: Motilal Banarsidass, 1990.

Yoga Vasistha: The Supreme Yoga. Swami Venkatesananda, trans. Shivanandanagar, Uttar Pradesh, India: Divine Life Society, 1976; 2nd ed., 1991.

JOURNALS

Ansari, R. A., *et al. Indian Journal of Medical Research,* 1988 87(4):401-4.

————. *Journal of Ethnopharmacology,* 1991 34(l):61-8.

Bhattacharya, S. K., *et al. Phytotherapy Research,* 1987 1(1):32-7.

Budhiraja, R. D., *et al. Indian Journal of Medical Research,* 1987 46(11):488-91.

Chakraborti, S. K, *et al. Experienta,* 1974 30(8):852-3.

Chander, *et al. Biochemical Pharmacology,* 1992 44(l):180-3

Dalvi, S. S., *et al. Journal of Postgraduate Medicine* (JS7), 1990 Apr. 36(2):91-4.

Das, H., *et al. Indian Journal of Cancer Chemotherapy,* 1985 7(2):56-65.

Dhir, *et al. Phytotherapy Research,* Vol. 4 NE5 1990:175.

Dorsch, W. *International Arch. Allergy Immunology*, 1992 99(2-4):493-5.
Dwivedi, *et al Phytotherapy Research.* 1991 5(3): 115-19.
Engels, *et al FEBS Letters*, 1992 305(3):254-6.
Ghosal, S., *et al Phytotherapy Research*, 1989 3(5):201-6.
Giri, A. K., *et al Cytologia* 51, 1986:375-80.
Jacob, A., *et al. European Journal of Clinical Nutrition* (EJC), 1988 Nov. 42(11):939-44.
Jain, *et al. Fitoterapia,* 1992 63(3):255-7.
Kazmi, S. U., *et al. Pakistan Journal of Pharmacological Science,* 1991 4(2):113-23.
Kim, J. S., *et al. Han'guk Nonghwa Hakhoechi,* Korea, 1993 36 (4):239-43.
Kloss, *et al Offen,* (German) 27 Jan 1972 16pp.
Kurokawa, M., *et al Antiviral Research Journal* 617, 1995 May 2(1-2):19-37.
Lee, S., *et al* (KRICT), *Arch. Pharmacological Research*, Korea, 1995 18(2):118-20.
Mahajani, S. S., *et al International Arch. Allergy Immunology,* 1976, 53(2):137-44.
Malhotra, C. L., *et al Indian Journal of Medical Research*, 1961 49:448-60.
———. *Indian Journal of Physicological Pharmacology*, 1960 4:49-64.
Mekkawy, S., *et al Chemical Pharmacy Bulletin*, Tokyo, CZP, 1995 Apr. 43(4):641-8.
Mhaiskar, V. B., *et al Rheumatism*, 1980 16(1):35-39.
"Modifying role of Phyllanthus," in *Cancer Letters*, NE59, Elsevier Scientific Publishers Ireland, Ltd. 1991:9-18.
Mohan Das, J., *et al. Indian Journal of Biochemistry*, 1964 1(3): 157-8.
Nalini, K, *et al Fitoterapie,* 1992 63(3):232-37.
Pandey, *et al.* Indian Journal of Physicological Pharmacology, 1989 33(1):47-52.
Parsad, S., *et al. Indian Journal of Physicological Pharmacology,* 1968 12(4):175-81. 1968
Phadke, S. A., *et al. Indian Journal of Medical Science* (GJP), 1989 May 43(5): 113-7.
Qiao, *et al Yaoxue Xuebao,* 1990 25(11):834-9.
Raghuunathan K, *et al. Indian Journal of Medical Research,* 1969 3(2):203-209.

Ram, G., *et al. Studying Biophysics,* 1984 103(1):37-40.

Rao, A. R. *International Journal of Cancer,* 1981 28: 607-10.

"Records of Usage or Assays in Phyllanthus," *Journal of Ethnopharmacology* NE 30, Elsevier Scientific Publishers Ireland Ltd., 1990:248-255.

Reddy, M. B., *et al. Indian Journal of Crude Drug Research,* 1988 26(4): 189-96.

Reddy, R. C., *et al. Fitoterapia,* vol. LXI NE 6 (1990):517-25.

Rege, N. N., *et al. Journal of Postgraduate Medicine,* (JS7) 1989 Oct. 35(4): 199-203.

————. *Journal of Postgraduate Medicine,* (JS7), 1993 Jan-Mar 39(1):22-5.

Rohrs, D., *Australian Journal of Medical Herbalism,* 1990 vol. 2(2):27-8.

Sadique, J., *et al. Acta Pharmacological Toxicology, Suppl.,* 1986 59(7):406-9.

Satyavati, G. V. *Indian Journal of Medical Research* 87, 1988 April pp. 327-35.

Shaila, H. P., *et al. International Journal of Cardiology,* (GQW) 1995 Apr. 49(2): 101-6.

Shukia, *et al. Journal of Ethnopharmacology,* 1987 21(1):65-74.

Shukla, B., *et al. Phytotherapy Research,* 1992 6(1):53-5.

Singh, N., *et al. Crude Drug Research,* 1978 16(1):8-16.

Somasundaram, S., *et al. Biochemical Medicine,* 1983 29(2):259-64.

Suthienkul, O. *Southeast Asian Journal of Tropical Medicine,* (UVN) 1993 Dec. 24(4):751-5.

Tariq, M., *et al. Indian Journal of Exploratory Biology,* 15 1977:485.

Thatte, U. M., *et al. Experimental Clinical Pharmacology* (LZN) 1988 Oct. 10(10):639-44.

Tiwari, A., *et al. Journal of Indian Medicine,* 2 (1968) 198.

Tobishi Pharmaceutical Co. *Kokai Tokkyo Koho* (Japanese) JP 59, 1984 April 28.

Index